Inspirational Poetry
for
Camp and Youth Groups

A COLLECTION OF VERSE

Compiled by

H. JEAN BERGER
Associate Professor
New York University
New York City

Illustrated by

HELEN MELROSE BULL
Assistant Professor of Art
State Teachers College
Cortland, New York

Burgess Publishing Company
Minneapolis 15, Minnesota

Fourth Edition 1964

1st Printing 1964
2nd Printing 1965
3rd Printing 1965

Library of Congress Catalog Card Number 58-10236

Printed in the United States of America

DEDICATION

Dedicated, in grateful appreciation,

to

my friends who have helped me

learn to love the out-of-doors

by sharing their bits of verse

with me through camp days and

inspirational services.

FOREWORD

Dear Reader:

In an effort to further poetry in the lives of young boys and girls as a medium of expression and inspiration, I have compiled a few of the poems from my poetry collection. It is hoped this compilation will reach camping enthusiasts and youth workers who may utilize these as an inspirational force when working with boys and girls.

It is my sincere desire that this collection may instigate poetry collections for youngsters, leaders, campers, and counselors who love the out-of-doors. My collection, now of two volumes, started as a camper many years ago and is one of my most cherished possessions. It says many things which cannot be found elsewhere since most of the poems came from individual collections which were shared during camp days.

May this compilation be but the beginning of a rich and valuable anthology which will be a joy to you and those with whom you work in the future.

H. Jean Berger

ACKNOWLEDGMENTS

The selections listed below are used by special arrangements with the following authorized publishers, editors, and individual holders of copyrights. Due credit is given to all authors of selections included in this anthology. Every effort has been made to locate copyright holders to give proper recognition to the authors for their work. Effort was made to obtain the source of those poems with unknown authors to grant recognition for their selections.

Doubleday and Company, Inc. for verses from "Song of the Open Road" from LEAVES OF GRASS by Walt Whitman; for "If" by Rudyard Kipling from REWARDS AND FAIRIES by Rudyard Kipling, copyright 1910 by Rudyard Kipling and reprinted by permission of Doubleday & Co., Inc. and Mrs. George Bambridge.

Charles Scribner's Sons for "Work" from THE POEMS OF HENRY VAN DYKE, copyright 1911 by Charles Scribner's Sons, 1939 by Tertius Van Dyke.

The Macmillan Company for "To A Camper", "Each Color or Tint That A Tree Has Known" by Mary S. Edgar from WOOD-FIRE AND CANDLELIGHT; for "Barter" and "The Coin" by Sara Teasdale; and for "A Chant Out of Doors" by Marguerite Wilkinson.

Dodd, Mead and Company for permission to use " I Meant To Do My Work Today" from THE LONELY DANCER by Richard LeGallienne. Copyright 1913, 1941 by Richard LeGallienne.

The Fidelity and Columbia Trust Company for "Which" by Cale Young Rice.

Harper and Brothers for "The Day" by Grace Noll Crowell; for "The Ways" and "Thank God For Work" by John Oxenham in SELECTED POEMS OF JOHN OXENHAM edited by C. L. Wallis, copyright by Erica Oxenham.

The Reilly and Lee Company for "It Couldn't Be Done" from THE COLLECTED VERSE OF EDGAR A. GUEST, copyright 1934 by The Reilly and Lee Company, Chicago; and for "Lord, Make A Regular Man Out Of Me" from THE LIGHT OF FAITH, copyright 1926 by The Reilly and Lee Company, Chicago.

Dr. Jay B. Nash for his lines "A Real Guide".

Camp Fire Girls, Inc. for "The Guardian's Credo" from the Leader's Certificate.

Unity School of Christianity for "This Is Friendship" by Mary Carolyn Davies.

E. P. Dutton and Company, Inc. for "The Silver Canoe" from I SING THE PIONEER by Arthur Guiterman, copyright 1926.

Mrs. Arthur Guiterman for "Canoe Trails" from THE MYRTHFUL LYRE by Arthur Guiterman.

Margaret Whalen for "She Stands in Silence" from vesper services at Huntington Memorial Camp, State Teachers College, Cortland, New York.

Anne Harris Robinson for "Sunset" from camp notes from Camp Aloha, Camp Fire Girls, Buffalo, New York.

Mr. Virgil Markham for "A Creed" and "Outwitted" by Edwin Markham.

Little, Brown and Company for "Not In Vain" and "We Never Know How High We Are" from THE POEMS OF EMILY DICKINSON by Martha Bianchi and Alfred Lee Hampsen, copyright 1944.

The YALE REVIEW for "Good Company" by Karle Wilson Baker, copyright Yale University Press.

Erica Oxenham for "The Sacrament of Fire" from THE TE DEUMS AND THE SACRAMENTS by her father, John Oxenham. Published by The Pilgrim Press, Boston, Mass.

Mary Thompson for "The Three Pines" from vesper services at Huntington Memorial Camp, State Teachers College, Cortland, New York.

Houghton Mifflin Company for "It Is My Joy In Life To Find" by Frank D. Sherman.

Abingdon Press for "I Give Thee Thanks" by Georgia Harkness from THE GLORY OF GOD, published by Abingdon Press, Nashville, Tenn. Copyright by Georgia Harkness, 1935.

Crown Publishers, Inc. for permission to use "Leaders" and "Adventure" from CHEERFUL CHERUB by Rebecca McCann, copyright, 1932 by Covici-Friede Publishers.

Mr. Ralph Hittman, Executive Director, Boys Brotherhood Republic of New York, 290 East Third Street, New York 9, New York for permission to use "The Power of Example".

Miss Emily Welch, Alexandria, Virginia for selections from her personal collection, "Lost October", Prairie", "A Word To The Living", "A Little Dream", and those selections written by her campers and staff at Camp Wabunaki, Douglas Hill, Maine.

Basilla E. Neilan, Director of Camps Elbanobscot and Teenobscot, Sudbury, Massachusetts for selections used in her camp which she shared.

Appreciation is expressed to formers counselors with whom I worked at Camp Sealth, Seattle-King County Council of Camp Fire Girls, Burton, Washington. Karen Edler, Elizabeth McIntire, Enid Liebinger, Nancy Legett have contributed original selections.

TABLE OF CONTENTS

Poetry in the Camp Program

To most children the initial experience at camp is one of the greatest adventures in their lives. It is a period of exploration in the out-of-doors, of getting acquainted with the animals, trees, flowers, and streams that are not seen in the city environment. Camp is the place where the group living process becomes extremely important and children learn to work and play together in a carefree environment under competent leaders.

Although most camps conduct different programs, dependent on the type of camp, each presents many common experiences to its campers. Each camp is deeply concerned about the child's health and safety, his physical well being, his emotional stability and social adjustment as well as his spiritual growth.

The spiritual life of a camper may be met through many different types of experiences. Mitchell and Crawford in CAMP COUNSELING* cite the following spiritual experiences occurring in most camps: a. grace before meals (oral, spoken in unison, sung, silence maintained through an appropriate musical selection, or a period of silent prayer); b. outdoor vespers; c. sunrise services; d. cabin devotions or meditations before taps; e. Sunday services in an outdoor chapel. Through these spiritual experiences in which the child may participate, poetry is one of the vital means of expression.

Children study poetry in school. They often write it as a means of expressing themselves, but many of them do not appreciate it until it can be associated with something close to them. In many schools, children become frightened.

---

*Mitchell, Viola and Crawford, Ida, CAMP COUNSELING. Philadelphia and London: W. B. Saunders Company, 1950. Ch. 16, p. 176.

of poetry, consider it sissy stuff, and are embarrassed to put into words what they feel about things. In camp, poetry can become a living thing which children accept because it is a means of expressing things which they feel about the out-of-doors and camp. Poetry, then, becomes a living thing. It no longer belongs to the past and the great masters as it often does in school. Four little lines may be the very thing that a child has longed to say or has felt but was reticent to put into words. Here is an inspiring medium in the life of children and young people which they may treasure the remainder of their lives. Poetry can be as effective a tool in camp as any activity which may be included in the camp program if it is conducted wisely.

Since the time young people first gathered before the fire in fellowship, poetry has been an influencing factor in the spiritual life of the camper. There is no history to trace the use of poetry and its values in camp, but a real camper learns this through thoughtful evenings before the fire, Sundays in camp, and special services that have provoked the use of poetry. For example, discussions about beauty, nature, friendship, democracy, individual worth, generosity, and other topics can be extolled in poetry and in many camps, this is done.

Poetry may be used in other areas of the camp program. Perhaps, for an evening camp fire, a counselor will recite her favorite poems or a camper will read one he had composed.

Campers often compose poems and songs about trips they have taken, their counselors, or special things in camp. Here is a creative medium that children feel free to use in an atmosphere where it is accepted.

It is important that poetry be readily accepted by the counselors and campers alike if it is to become an integral part of the program. It is especially necessary that counselors show an interest in and an understanding for this medium of expression. A camp may utilize poetry and have it become one of the most fascinating things a camper experiences in this setting. Not only will it have an influence on the child at camp, but it may enable him to have a greater appreciation for it when he returns to school in the fall.

Many camp directors request staff members to bring poetry collections to camp with them. This seems to set the stage and the campers more readily accept it after seeing the pleasure and satisfaction their counselors receive from their collections. Some camps have a poetry corner where favorite poetry books are kept and counselors and campers may leave their collections for camper perusal and the exchange of poems. Many a camper has departed from camp with a favorite selection of poems which has been enlarged in following summers. A few camps engage a counselor for creative writing whose main responsibility is to help children express themselves. This may be done through the creation of songs, stories, poems, or a camp newspaper. This special counselor must have the ability to make poetry alive to children; one who can interest them in this medium whether on a hike, around the craft table, on a canoe trip, or in the quiet of the day.

One enthusiastic leader can do much to start an awareness for camp poetry. This may be contagious and spread until the entire camp is enjoying bits of verse which express a feeling, or a mood about the camp situation or daily living experiences.

One of the most impressive experiences for children is a program known as "Magic Ring". This usually is held around the camp fire in the dark. Each youngster and leader contributes a bit of verse, his favorite poem, or a thought until each has made his contribution. The important thing is not to break the chain by a lapse of silence. Sometimes it is done with songs and poetry, each child deciding which he will use. Many times "Magic Ring" becomes the time when a child will speak of something very personal to him before a large group. It is a time when campers sit around the fire and meditate about the poems and thoughts of others. Through my years of camp experience, I have seen such a ceremony impress college students as well as younger children. "Magic Ring" is a ceremony which was used in one of the camps on the West Coast for many years and was so sacred to these campers that they decided to compile an anthology of the poems that had been recited. This collection was published and is one of the finest collections of camp poetry. Unfortunately, it is out of print and difficult to obtain. It is a book that should be in every camp library as it is so inclusive in its scope of poems. The book is entitled MAGIC RING because it grew from the magic rings of hundreds of girls in camp.

Another excellent book for camp use is NATURE LOVER'S KNAPSACK by Edwin O. Grover. This book is also the result of a person's love for poems that expressed those thoughts which reminded him of past pleasures and present joys found in the world about him. This anthology was compiled and published for the sole purpose of sharing these poems with others.

Both MAGIC RING and NATURE LOVER'S KNAPSACK have a wealth of poems about nature, the open road, friendship trees, vagabondia, the sea, and other areas that are appropriate for a camp program.

Perhaps the truest measure of success in this phase of a camp program is the number of youngsters who suddenly develop an enthusiasm for hearing, writing, and reading poetry as well as starting their own personal collection. How can a child who has lived in the woods read Mary S. Edgar's "To A Camper" and not have a heart full of recollection and thoughts of a pleasant past? How then, can that child ever disassociate herself from that poem? It is in this manner that poetry can become an important part of a child's life at camp, both spiritually and creatively.

This medium may be one which many times is neglected at home and in school as a part of the child's spiritual growth. There are people who feel that poetry and sentimentality are synonomous. There are those people who feel that sentimentality is a trait of weakness, with the result that some people are afraid to show an active interest in poetry. Such an interest surely can be an attribute to an individual's spiritual life, and camp is one of the finest environments in which to develop this interest.

Let's have more poetry corners, more poetry collections, that we, campers and counselors, may look back upon and recall with ecstasy those pleasant memories and associations of days spent along the woodland trail!

MAGIC RING

This is my ring of magic,

My heart is tied within.

Leave these pages lying calm,

You who would glance and grin.

Oft when the stars would shine

Above the camp fire glow,

This book's soul sang with memories,

Songs and ballads hummed peacefully low.

No matter what the years take and bring,

He is young who knows the secrets of
Magic Ring.

This is my ring of magic,

Time has left it undimmed.

Throw down your load, please stop awhile

And pass with me within.

From Miss Danny's
Magic Ring
Camp Sealth, 1958

...of Camp

TO A CAMPER

You may think my dear, when you grow quite old
You have left camp days behind
But I know the scent of wood smoke
Will always call to mind
Little paths at twilight
And trails you used to find.

You may think some day you are quite grown up
And feel so worldly wise
But suddenly from out of the past
A vision will arise
Of merry folk with brown bare knees
And laughter in their eyes.

You may live in a house, built to your taste
In the nicest part of town
But someday for your old camp togs
You'd change your latest gown
And trade it for a balsam bed
Where stars all night look down.

You may find yourself grown wealthy
Have all that gold could buy
But you'd toss aside a fortune
For days 'neath an open sky
With sunlight on blue waters
And white clouds floating high.

For once you have been a camper
Then something has come to stay
Deep in your heart forever
Which nothing can take away
And heaven can only be heaven
With a camp in which to play.

Mary S. Edgar

WHEN YOU LEAVE CAMP

The friendly little path I know
Will miss your glad young feet;
The hillsides and the forests
The sound of laughter sweet;
The dancing waves upon the lake
Will miss canoe and sail;
All silent in the shadowed woods
Will be your well-worn trail.

The singing birds will miss your songs
The stars your wondering eyes;
The ever-changing sunsets
Your look of hushed surprise.
You leave behind the beauty
Of all the hills you trod,
But in your heart you take away
More lasting gifts of God.

Author Unknown

THE END OF A PERFECT DAY

A camp in the woods beside a stream
When the evening sun is low;
A place and a time when one can dream
In the firelights friendly glow.
The charm of mystic symphony
That the woodland creatures play;
And you enjoy it all with me
That, the end of a perfect day.

Author Unknown

I AM CAMP

I am camp - I am sunlight, a sheen on the
water, a mist on the mountains and stars.
I am a doorway out of the commonplace
into a new adventuring experience.
I am a place where youth learns the joy of play
without sting, of fellowship without regrets,
of creative effort that wearies not, of a good
time that leaves no headache, or heartache,
behind. I am a new purpose for life that will
make the year different. I am voice and silence
with a thrill to it. I am laughter, and quiet
resolution that seeks the comfort of the hills.
I am energy and the touch of loving service.
I am youth and the slowly emerging habits that
make mature experience worthy.
I am today and also the tomorrow that is being
shaped.
I am a Giver of Gifts that will not pass away,
that time will not chill and poverty will not
quench, that riches will not deceive.
I am habits, ideals, ways of living, confirmed
attitudes in the Soul of Youth. Because I am
all these and more, I invite you into fellowship
with me. I am camp.

Beatrice Cowan
Highlights, YWCA

END OF CAMP

It's never good-bye when a summer camp ends,
You just inventory your good times and friends,
And store them away in your memory marked "Keep".
Then, through the long winter, what pleasures
you reap....

Remembering!

Author Unknown

COMRADES OF THE TRAIL

Until the day the world shall die
We shall be comrades you and I.

For we have seen the morning break
In golden beauty on that lake
That rests with intimate grace before
Our cedar cabin's unlatched door;
And we have heard the rain at night
And blessed our driftwood hearth-fire light;
Wakened by thunder we have crept
Closer and turned again and slept
While the trees crashed, weakening,
And blocked our trail up to the spring.

Dangers of cities never draw
Two close as does the forest's awe;
Beauties of cities never bind
Memory and heart and soul and mind
As does the dawn in forest places,
Or tree-rent moonlight on our faces.

Husband and wife! If that were all!
Not vows alone have made us thrall,
But none can evermore walk free
Bound to each other as are we,
By sky and water, fern and tree.

Mary Carolyn Davies

HELP WANTED

Wanted:

A girl for the summer months
A girl who can really play,
Who can take the wheel of steed or steel
And point her up woodland way.

A girl who can hike, a girl who can fish.
A girl who can cast a dry fly,
Or if she can't do it, will gamely stick to it
And wins out or wants to know why.

A girl who can whistle, a girl who can sing
And laugh when the tent springs a leak,
Who can swing a good paddle, or ride a horse straddle
And powder her nose once a week.

A girl who loves moonlight, and isn't afraid
Of small creatures that roam in the night
Who can strike a match man-style
That is, if there's no one in sight.

Wanted:

A girl for the summer months,
One qualified, please apply,
Then perhaps in cold weather, we'll still trail together
And only break camp when we die.

Author Unknown

OLD SHOES

A city closet is no place for -
    Half mocassin, grotesquely flat and wide!
I could not wear you on the avenue.
    With peasant awkwardness you rest beside
Aristocratic heels. But once we stood
    Before a cataract that tossed the spray
On mossy banks; we tramped a fragrant wood
    Where earth was like an incense, and our way
Was intercepted by a tree that bent
    Its forehead to the ground as if in prayer.
Through heavy boughs the sun was reverent,
    And silent benediction filled the air.
Discard you? No! You bring me dreams,
    And then,
Sometime we may go tramping off again.

Gertrude Bennett

THE OUTDOOR GIRL

The outdoor girl is one who loves all living things
    Enough to go where nature flings
Her beauties round about
    And dwell with them awhile;
Must be when she comes back once more
    A little better than before
A little surer of her faith
    A little readier to smile.

Author Unknown

TO A CHILD

Every child should know a hill
And the clean joy of running down its long slope
with the wind in his hair.
He should know a tree - the comfort of its cool
lap of shade,
And the supple strength of its arms,
balancing him between the earth and sky.
So he is a creature of both,
He should know bits of singing water - the
strange mysteries of its depth,
And the long sweet grasses that border it.
Every child should know some scrap of uninterrupted
sky to shout against;
And have one star dependable and bright for
wishing on.

Edna Casler Joll

OUR CAMP

Our camp is nestled in the Northland,
Built for us by our Father's hand.
All our days we sing in praise,
Of its shining waters and its forest land.
We see our friends every day,
Learning so much about work and play.
Not a day goes by without having fun,
Playing freely beneath God's sun.
We see each other when work is done,
Growing stronger with goals soon won.
We see the forest and the lake so blue,
Ever calling to me and you.
Home of nature and our pleasures new,
Land of splendor and beauty, too.

Mary Lou Altmann,
Camper
State University College Camp
Cortland, New York

THE SPIRIT'S JUST THE SAME

The trail is just a little wider,
And where are the cabins down by the shore?
I don't remember this building here,
And what did they cut the trees down for?

The faces don't look familiar,
And some of the songs, they're singing wrong.
We didn't take the trips they do.
Have I really been away from camp that long?

Traditions seem a trifle tangled,
And the clearing up there has a different name.
But none of these things really matter,
Because the spirit's just the same.

Author Unknown
From a Candlelight Dinner
Camp Sealth, 1958

WHAT IS THE TIE

What is the tie that binds us
Friends of the long, long trail?
Just this . . .
We have shared the weather,
We have slumbered side by side,
And friends who have camped together
Can never again divide.

Author Unknown

HEART'S DESIRE

Have you ever watched a camp fire
When the wood has fallen low,
And the ashes start to whiten
'Round the embers crimson glow?

With the night sounds all around you
Making silence doubly sweet,
And a high full moon above you
That the spell may be complete?

Tell me! Were you ever nearer
To the land of heart's desire
Than when you sat there thinking
With your feet before the fire?

Virginia Eaton

CAMP

To sleep in the open
Under the sweet smelling pine, and
To feel the thrill of dawn -
This is camp, camp is for you.

Mildred Casey
Camp Fire Director

A PRAYER OF A CAMPER

God of the Hills, grant me strength to go back to the cities
without faltering -
Strength to do my daily task without tiring and with enthusiasm,
Strength to help my neighbor who has no hills to remember.

God of the Lake, grant me thy peace and thy restfulness,
Peace to bring into the world of hurry and confusion.

God of the Stars, may I take back the gift of friendship, of
love for all.
Fill me with the breadth and the depth and heighth of the
wilderness
By every thought and word and need.

Irene Mott

BLACK BUGS

Black bugs in the water,
Red ants everywhere,
Chiggers round our waistline,
Sand flies in our hair -
But the dust of cities
At any cost we shun,
And cry amid our itchings,
"Isn't camping fun?"

Alice Armiger Skeen

SHE STANDS IN SILENCE

She stands in silence

With head held high.

Her boundary fences

The earth and sky.

This is a picture of a girl who has gotten from camp all the worthwhile things.

A girl who has learned to appreciate ... the rosy glow of sunset; the mist, as it winds and scarves through the woodland; the wind, as it whispers in soft conversation with the leaves; the blueness of evening; the stars as they grow smaller and paler; the meadow silver with dew. In short, the simple unadorned beauty of God's own earth, wind and trees, sun, moon, and stars.

A girl who knows that camp is a chapter in the Book of Life, rich with real wonder of human relationships ... that camp is the finest place to live in, grow in, to learn to give oneself, to know the true self of others, to be with God in his own setting.

A girl who knows how to stand in silence

With head held high ... a girl whose

Boundary fences <u>are</u> the earth and sky.

Margaret Whalen, Camper
State Teachers College Camp
Cortland, New York

SONG OF THE OPEN ROAD

Afoot and light-hearted I take to the open road,

Healthy, free, the world before me,

The long brown path before me leading wherever I choose.

Henceforth, I ask not good fortune, I myself am good fortune,

Henceforth, I whimper no more, postpone no more, need

nothing,

Done with indoor complaints, libraries, querulous criticisms,

Strong and content - I travel the open road.

Walt Whitman

ADVENTURE

Each man gets as much from adventure as to

the adventure he brings,

For things don't happen to people, it's

people who happen to things.

Rebecca McCann

DEAR CAMP DIRECTOR

He means so very much to us
This child of ours you borrow.
He' s the only one we' ve got,
Sole gift to the tomorrow.

We gladly loan him to you
For we know at camp he'll grow.
You'll find him very eager
There' s much he wants to know.

We know you' ll treat him kindly
As he explores the hills,
And fills his heart with wonder
And fills his day with thrills.

But most of all we pray you,
Please do not think us odd.
We hope at camp he'll practice
Close fellowship with God.

Written by Walter MacPeek
who was sending his child
to camp for the first time.

REMEMBER

She may be a monster,
She may be a brat,
But, she's somebody' s darling ...
Remember that!

Marilyn Thomas
Counselor,
Camp Sealth, 1954

GIVE ME A PLACE

Oh, give me a place
By the side of a stream.
Let the pine trees wave above.
I shall not ask for any wealth
Nor shall I ask for love,

For all I want
Of earthly things
Are the needles under my feet,
And all of heaven a patch of sky
Where green plumes meet.

I long for a spot
Where the roar of the falls
And the wind makes harmony,
Where the pine trees lifting giant arms
Conduct the symphony.

Author Unknown

FOLLOW, DREAM, AND ...

Follow the winding pathways through the forest.
Follow the gentle streams to lakes of blue.
Follow the star that gleams at evening
When day is through, when day is through.

Dream of the day that passed before us.
Dream of the Indian-fire' s glow.
Dream of the sound of laden voices
Chanting low, chanting low.

Bring the woodland songs into the city,
Bring the gleam of stars to tired eyes.
Bring home the pathways of tomorrow
From the skies, from the skies.

Author Unknown

A CHANT OUT OF DOORS

God of grave nights,
God of brave mornings,
God of silent noon,
Hear my salutation!

For where the rapids rage white and scornful,
I have passed safely, filled with wonder;
Where the sweet pools dream under willows,
I have been swimming, filled with life.

God of round hills,
God of green valleys,
God of clear springs,
Hear my salutation!

For where the moose feeds, I have eaten berries.
Where the moose drinks, I have drunk deep.
When the storms crash through broken heavens -
And under clear skies - I have known joy.

God of great trees,
God of wild grasses,
God of little flowers,
Hear my salutation!

For where the deer crops and the beaver plunges,
Near the river I have pitched my tent;
Where the pines cast aromatic needles
On a still floor, I have known peace.

God of grave nights,
God of brave mornings,
God of silent noon,
Hear my salutation!

Marguerite Wilkinson

MY CREED OF THE OUT-OF-DOORS

I believe in the wonder of the out-of-doors,
In the inspiration of the stars,
And in the allurement of life in the open.

I believe in the strength of the hills,
In the silence of the night,
And in the music of the birds and trees.

I believe that my body was made for action,
That my mind was made for thinking,
And that my heart was made for loving
In unison with the life in Nature.

I believe that to laugh and sing,
To swim and walk, to study and play,
To eat and be happy, to be kind and free,
To grow strong and good is my God-given-right.

I believe that to be happy, I must be good,
That to be worthy, I must be kind,
That to be loved, I must think love.

I believe that God is as near as man,
That I can hear Him in the brooks and pines.
And that happiness and lasting peace are mine,
As I live in the atmosphere of kindness,
So near me in the life of the open road.

Rudolph Carl Stroll

A CAMP FIRE

A Camp Fire is such a friendly thing, whether it is a small one built for only two or three persons or whether it is a large one, sending its glow upon all surroundings and transforming them into bizarre shapes and images. There is something in the heart of a fire, flickering tongues of flame, or in the darker, steadier glow of the coals, which makes all people one, uniting them in the fellowship of the fire.

What fascination there is in watching the tiny flame-spirits retreat and advance as they frolic over the firewood! Sometimes they leap out a little farther, and then hurriedly skip back, as if they feared they had been too bold.

What comfort the lonely traveler can find in having his evening meal around a heap of glowing coals! How much nearer it draws him to the stars which had seemed cold and distant before and how it lightens the burden of the darkness which had been so oppressive!

Author Unknown

AS YOU THIS FIRE HAVE KINDLED

"As you this fire have kindled, may
Its flame be fed by fuel that, with willing hands,
You gather in the fields and open lands.
It's back-log, courage for your lofty aims;
The flickering flames are love of forest trails;
And in the heart of the embers, burning deep,
The love of home and hearth-side may you keep
To glow more brightly tho' the flame's light fails.

You will go on along your forest way,
The trail you follow may be traced by fires
That you have kindled through your high desires,
And golden dreams you dream everyday.
Oh, may the dreams you dream in passing by,
Burn clear and true against your evening sky!"

Elizabeth Collom

EACH COLOR OR TINT THAT A TREE HAS KNOWN

Each color or tint that a tree has known
In the heart of a wood-fire glows.
Look into the flames and you will see
Blue dusk and the dawn's pale rose,
The golden light of the noonday sun,
The purple of darkening night,
The crimson glow of the sunset,
The sheen of the soft moonlight.

Fire brings forth from the heart of a tree
Beauty stored there in memory.

Mary S. Edgar

THE SACRAMENT OF FIRE

Kneel always when you light a fire!
Kneel reverently and thankful be
For God's unfailing charity,
And on the ascending flame inspire
A little prayer, that shall upbear
The incense of your thankfulness
For this sweet grace
Of warmth and light!
For here again is sacrifice
For your delight.

Within the wood,
That lived a joyous life
Through sunny days and rainy days
And winter storms and strife; -
Within the peat,
That drank the moorland sweet
Of bracken, whin, and sweet bell-heather,
And all the joy of gold gorse feather
Flaming like Love in wintriest weather, -
While snug below, in sun and snow,
Peat heard the beat of the padding feet
Of foal and dam, and ewe and lamb,
And the stamp of old bell-wether; -
Within the coal,
Where forests lie entombed,
Oak, elm, chestnut, beech, and red pine bole, -
God shrined His sunshine and enwombed
For you these stores of light and heat,
Your life-joys to complete.

These all have died that you might live;
Yours now the high prerogative
To loose their long captivities, -
To give them new sweet span of life
And fresh activities.

Kneel always when you light a fire!
Kneel reverently,
And grateful be
To God for His unfailing charity!

John Oxenham from
THE TE DEUMS AND THE SACRAMENTS

WHAT IS FIRE?

What is fire? A fire is wood, gathered from many places, which, when lit by a single match, flares up and brings us warmth and light. But to anyone who has ever been to camp, a fire is something more. It is a symbol and stands for another fire of a different kind, which burns in the hearts of all of us. Here at camp, we are the wood, and although we are gathered from many different homes, the flame of a single person or idea, can set us all ablaze. Then we ourselves may be the dancing fire, as we play something entertaining or simply funny, or we may be the more quiet, flickering fire which brings us peace after a busy day. But we are the fire, a single flame created of many sources, and when we leave camp, we carry, each of us as we go our separate ways, a bit of Kilowan fire burning inside us.

Camp Fire Girl,
Camp Kilowan
Albany, Oregon

CANOE TRAILS

Broad is the track that the steamer takes
    Over the open sea.
Wide are the waves of the windy lake,
    Dear are the lakes to me.
And the sparkling sound is good,
    Bright is the river too;
But the stream that winds to the heart of the woods
    Is the trail of the little canoe.

Up through the fields where cattle browse,
    Up through farms of rye,
Under the arching hemlock boughs,
    Under the laughing sky,
Out through the maze where the muskrats hide,
    Drawn like a silver clue,
Clear to the buttressed mountain-side
    Goes the trail of the little canoe.

Clean blue flags in stately ranks
    Stand where the shallows gleam;
Ferns grow thick on the mossy banks
    Edging the deeper stream;
Tanagers flash in the vaulted leaves
    Where, faint shimmering through,
A drowsy pattern the sunlight weaves
    On the trail of the little canoe.

Dip of the paddles gurgle and plash,
    Quiet the bird-note clear,
White of the birch, grey of the ash ---
    Balm of the heart is here!
Here where the boulder footpaths cease,
    Here where the best is true,
The loveliest road to the shrines of peace
    Is the trail of the little canoe.

Arthur Guiterman

TEN COMMANDMENTS OF HEALTH

1. Honor thy morning dip and daily swim.

2. Remember thy water to drink it daily - seven glasses shalt thou drink and the eighth thou shalt drink also.

3. When nature calls, do not attempt to bluff her, but haste away without delay, or else your health will suffer.

4. Honor thy womanliness that thou mayst be brave for days that are to come.

5. Thou shalt show mercy unto thy muscles. Play and work hard but do not overtax them.

6. Thou shalt have perfect posture at all times. Do not slump, always remembering, never forgetting that dreaded hump.

7. Thou shalt not kiss for she who so doeth endangereth her fellow campers.

8. Thou shalt not envy thy friends boxes from home, neither shalt thou partake of them.

9. Thou shalt not disturb thy tent mates rest after the lights out bell, or before the rising bell.

10. Honor thy soap and water. Wash many times daily, for she who doeth this doth not endangereth herself to Poison Ivy and woe unto her who contracts this plague for she shall be marked unclean.

Nurse Loretta
Camp Miniwanca, 1934

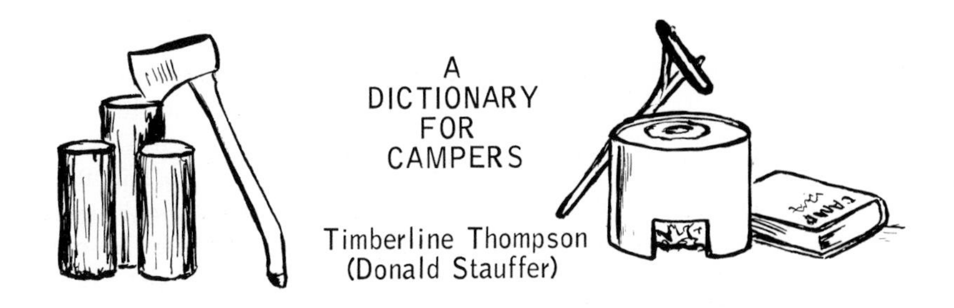

A DICTIONARY FOR CAMPERS

Timberline Thompson
(Donald Stauffer)

AX: An ax is a piece of metal sharpened at one end and attached at the other end to a piece of wood. When small, an ax is called a hatchet and is used for an ornament suspended from the belt, making the wearer look camp-like, just as colored neckerchieves and bowie knives and ivy rashes do. The correct and most common way to use the word ax in a sentence is this: "Where is the ax?"

BACON: Bacon is that edible substance which has saved most amateur campers from starving to death. It is made from pigs and comes in striped slices. Some people like it transparent, like angleworms; others like it crisp, like dog-biscuits. When most campers run out of bacon, they either run back to town and get some more, or they run around naked through the woods searching for wild boar and living on roots and berries.

BALSAM BED: A balsam bed is made out of maple leaves, spruce tips, pine needles, and an old hair mattress; hence, it's name, balsam bed. Some people consider that balsam beds should be made only from the branches of a balsam tree. That is an awful error, since there is no more reason for saying that balsam beds are made to sleep in which certainly is not true: witness flower beds, folding beds, and the bed of the ocean. The balsam tree may be recognized by its bark. To hear a whole forest of balsam trees barking at once is a surprise which has delighted only a few campers.

BLANKETS: Blankets come in two sizes: those not long enough and those six inches too short. When you sleep double, blankets are the things that keep the other fellow warm at night. If you sleep single, you should roll up in the same direction, and you should then make a note in your book of which direction you must roll in the morning to untangle yourself. Many a man otherwise healthy has rolled himself desperate because he could not remember which way he should turn to get the blankets off. When sleeping on the side of a mountain, always roll into your blankets downhill, so that if you should consider rolling during the night, your blankets will keep close about you, as otherwise it would be inconvenient to roll clear to the foot of the mountain and then have to climb back for the blankets.

CAMERA: A camera is a big joke on the photographer. The theory of the camera is that it reproduces what it sees. I guess it does. Some day some genius will invent a camera that will reproduce what the photographer wants it to see. Here are some rules for operating the camera. Don't hold your thumb over the shutter opening. Don't take more than two or three pictures on the same film; it may seem like economy but it is likely to blur the picture. Never point the camera at yourself; your vest button is interesting only when it comes off.

CAMP FIRE: The camp fire is a peculiar sort of fire that is never hot enough to raise the biscuits but always hot enough to make it uncomfortable for the cooks. It should be started with not more than two matches. If you use more than two you are not a good scout but you have my sympathy, Pard, for I can't do it either. To start a camp fire, whittle up a big pile of shavings, get a heap of old timber over your material, soak the pile thoroughly in very dry kerosene, and then use your box of matches trying to light it. After that, walk the fifteen miles back to the village and buy a gasoline stove or some canned heat.

CAMP SITE: A camp site is a place where you get too tired to go any further and yell, "Eureka, here's a great place to camp". It isn't. It never is. No one has been born that could find a camp site that wasn't muddy or rocky or prickly or damp or bumpy or rolly or sloping the wrong way. Daniel Boone once said, "Show me the man who can pick a good camp site every time and I will show you a liar". After finding the rockiest place in camp, pitch your tent right over it, then spread your blankets smoothly over the sharp points of the rocks and then go to sleep in a tree.

CANTEEN: A canteen is a hollow metal utensil with a mouth at the top and a leak at the bottom.

COOKING UTENSIL: Those utensils in which one cooks vegetables is termed in camp language "cooking utensils". A frying pan may be recognized by the fact that the last cook forgot to wash it in hot water. A coffee pot is built with a long nose for pouring and a big handle, with the result that it will never nest in between the other utensils. A Dutch oven looks like a combination of a waffle iron and a grafonola and is about the weight of a nice sturdy safe. A reflector oven is a sort of three sided collapsible windmill, and is so called because it broods and reflects on how long it should stay open, finally collapsing just as the biscuits or cornpone is just beginning to brown on top. Similarly, the stew kettle, usually an old lard pail, is hung by its bale which is soldered on and rarely melts off until the soup or stew is almost cooked.

FIELD GLASSES: A field glass is a device for bringing the background into the foreground by looking into the foreground through two holes. Field glasses are useful for detecting wild life on a dog's back or portions of steak on a

boarding house platter. When one is pursued closely by a mad grizzly bear it is suggested that one take out his field glasses and regard the bear calmly through the wrong ends. The grizzly will appear the size of a chipmunk, and one will appear perfectly safe and contented. The mad bear upon approach will see through the right end of the glasses and will take one for a super man. Disgruntled and baffled, the grizzly will withdraw whimpering with rage.

FORD: In Kit Carson's day, a Ford was a place where you could cross the river. Now a Ford is what you have to get out of and change the wheels which are known as the drop rim. This pleasant diversion adds an unusually joyous note when performed at the last minute just before starting home. Everything has been packed in the Ford and you sing happily as you remove them all to get the wrench and jack which are at the bottom. It might be classed as the modern camper's burro and pack horse.

KNAPSACK: So called from the famous Knap who discovered the North Pole of the pretzel. The knapsack is worn on the back like a reversible bib and every time you bend over forward, it flops up over your shoulders and knocks your hat off. The knapsack is made to carry the small personal belongings of the hiker, such as toothbrush, mineral specimens, flashlight, flatiron, soda crackers, darning yarn, pencil and memo book, field glasses, two chocolate bars, etc., etc., etc.. In packing the knapsack, care should be taken to put all the necessities in the bottom.

KNIFE: A handy thing to have around camp. May be used for cutting macroni into suckable lengths, opening tinned meats when the patent key won't work, playing mumble-de-peg, paring the toe nails, or just general whittling. Caution: be sure and close the blades before returning the knife to the pocket.

LIFE-LINE: A forty foot piece by which the climbers on precipes and glaciers are tied together, so that if one man slips and falls down a crevice, the whole party will keep him company.

SWEATER: A sweater is a stretchy thing with two sleeves, and a button missing. It is tied around the waist and flaps up and down during the hot part of the hike, and then someone else borrows it just as it begins to get cold. By getting an extra large sweater it is possible for two to wear it at the same time. This saves the price of the second sweater.

WATCH: A watch is a rather small object that tells what time it is, and makes an infernal racket doing it, too, particularly if it is under your pillow. If you keep it in your pocket all night, it makes you sleep very lumpy in spots, and if you take it out and put it on the cold ground, it stops. The best watch for the camper is a watch with radium hands so that when one wakes up at three o'clock in the morning one can tell what time it is unless there's something wrong with one's eyes... or watch. Another way to tell the time in the night is to count the ticks and subtract them from the hour the watch says when it is light enough to see.

WEAPON: Under this general heading is included such instruments of self-protection as revolvers, empty canteens, BB guns, spitballs, beanies, and pencil sharpeners. An ingenious camper is never at a loss for a weapon to protect himself against the native savages and wild beasts. Chewing gum, for example, is a deadly weapon which has been used against many wild animals, such as the pink-eyed puma. When pursued by a pink-eyed puma, calmly stand your ground, and as the puma springs, insert an unwrapped stick of chewing gum on each of its four incisors. Astonished at this clever maneuver and baffled at the guminess of its jaws, the pink-eyed puma will slink away enveloped in a strong odor of pepsin.

WOODSMAN: A good woodsman has been defined as a fellow you would like to go camping with - again. A good woodsman is as hard to find as a good camp-site, but when you find one, take Timberline Thompson's advice and hold onto him. Show him this dictionary and if he doesn't believe a word of it, he's all there.

...of Beauty and Nature

GOD, THE ARTIST

God, when you thought of a pine tree,
How did you think of a star?
How did you think of a damson west,
Crossed by an inky bar?
How did you think of a dear brown pool
Where flocks of shadows are?

God, when you thought of a cob web,
How did you think of the dew?
How did you know a spider's house
Had spangles bright and new?
How did you know we human folk
Would love them as we do?

God, when you patterned a bird song,
Flung on a silver string,
How did you know the ecstasy
That crystal call would bring?
How did you think of a bubbling throat
And a daring speckled wing?

God, when you chiseled a rain drop,
How did you think of a stem,
Bearing a lovely satin leaf
To hold the tiny gem?
How did you know a million drops
Would deck the morning's hem?

Why did you make the moonlight night
With honeysuckle vines?
How did you know maderia bloom
Distilled ecstatic wines?
How did you weave the velvet dusk
Where tangled perfumes are?
God, when you thought of a pine tree
How did you think of a star?

Angela Morgan

THE DAY WILL BRING SOME LOVELY THING

The day will bring some lovely thing,
I say it over each new dawn -
Some gay, adventureous thing to hold
Within my heart when it is gone,
And so I rise and go to meet
The day, with wings upon my feet.

I come upon it unaware,
Some hidden beauty, without name,
A snatch of song, a breath of pine,
A poem lit with golden flame,
High-tangled bird notes, keenly thinned,
Like flying color in the wind.

No day has ever failed me quite;
Before the grayest day is done,
I come upon some misty bloom,
Or a late line of crimson sun.
Each night, I pause, remembering
Some gay, adventureous, lovely thing.

Grace Noll Crowell

BEAUTY

"Sometimes I think dear, that the only permanent thing in life is beauty. I don't mean the beauty you can see, I mean the beauty of love, the beauty of integrity, the beauty of courage. Oh, my children! There are so many beauties!"

Author Unknown
From a magazine story.

BARTER

Life has loveliness to sell -

All beautiful and splendid things

Blue waves whitened on a cliff,

Climbing fire that sways and sings,

And children faces looking up

Holding wonder like a cup.

Life has loveliness to sell -

Music like a curve of gold,

Scent of pine trees in the rain,

Eyes that love you, arms that hold,

And for your spirits still delight

Holy thoughts that star the night.

Spend all you have for loveliness,

Buy it and never count the cost;

For one white singing hour of peace

Count many a year of strife well lost,

And for a breath of ecstasy

Give all you have been or could be.

Sara Teasdale

HE HAS NOT LIVED

He has not lived who has not known

The springing sod beneath his heels,

Or seen against a bank of clouds

A lone brave eagle soar and wheel.

He has not lived who has not known

Where lacy willows dream and laugh,

Or seen the lightening rend an oak

As breezes drive away the chaff.

His life is incomplete if he

Has never seen beyond a star,

Or heard a river's murmurings

From a distant, sandy bar.

Margaret Crisler
Camp Wakitatina,
Waco, Texas

THE WORLD IS MINE

Today, upon a bus, I saw
A lovely maid with golden hair.
I envied her, she seemed so gay ...
And, oh, I wished I were so fair.
When suddenly, she rose to leave,
I saw her hobble down the aisle.
She had one foot and wore a crutch
But, as she passed, a smile.
Oh, God, forgive me when I whine.
I have two feet, the world is mine.

And when I stopped to buy some sweets,
The lad who served me had such charm,
He seemed to radiate good cheer.
I said, "It's nice to deal with you,
Such courtesy I seldom find."
He turned and said, "Oh, thank you, sir!"
And then I saw that he was blind.
Oh, God, forgive me when I whine.
I have two eyes, the world is mine.

Then, when walking down the street,
I saw a child with eyes of blue.
He stood and watched the others play.
It seemed he knew not what to do.
I stood a moment, then I said,
"Why can't you join the others, dear?"
He looked ahead without a word,
And then I knew, he could not hear.
Oh, God, forgive me when I whine.
I have two ears, the world is mine.

With feet to take me where'd I'd go,
With eyes to see the sunset's glow,
With ears to hear what I should know,
I'm blessed indeed. The world is mine!
Oh, God, forgive me when I whine.

Elizabeth McIntire
Camp Sealth Counselor, 1959

GOD'S GOLD

When picking up a clod of earth
    Consider what you hold:
A treasure of the greatest worth,
    Far more than miser's gold.

A tiny seed in its embrace
    Sends up a living shoot.
There's beauty in a pansy's face
    And wealth around its roots.

This clod may hold a wealth of food
    Or clothing for a score.
When God made earth He called it good;
    Why should I ask for more?

Today I hold it in my hands,
    Tomorrow it holds me;
And now, at last, I understand
    About eternity.

Loren W. Burch

BEAUTY

Swing the night over me, beauty.
I, who have followed you far,
Rest where my feet have stumbled
Over a phantom bar.

Let your tears fall on my eyelids,
This moment I must not dream.
Halfway between dusk and dawning,
Smooth out tomorrow's seam.

In this eternal moment,
I, who followed you far,
Presently shall discover
Easier steps to your star.

Author Unknown

STRANGE THE THINGS YOU CAN'T FORGET

Strange the things you can't forget.
The scent of grass new-mown, and earth rain wet.
Little things, like autumn's leaves
Drifting on still air in the golden sheaves;
Lovely things, like twilight's gloom
And the silence that hangs in an empty room.
Books lying open, ready to your hand,
And time spinning out its rationed sand.
Lamplight on silver; moonlight on the lawn;
The house when you're left in it, forsaken, forlorn.
Sad things, like partings and greetings withheld,
And kindness forgotten or sweetness repelled...
    There's so much that is new to remember, and yet
    It's strange the things you can't forget.

Elizabeth Webb

SUMMER STAIN

The loveliness that trembles
From grasses bright with dew;
Or glows with fire of opal
Above the darkened view;

That wakes in black and silver
When lightenings weave the night;
Or drowses in the noonday
In clearings drenched with light;

That sweeps with brush prismatic
The curtain of the rain;
And dims with wash of azure
Far hills and distant main;

That sleeps in troubled crystal
Where mountain torrents halt;
And streams, a starry river,
Across the airy vault;

This shall forever color
Our minds with beauty's stain,
Who roams the hills of summer
With sun and stars and rain.

Pierson Curtis, Counselor
Camp Wabunaki
Douglas Hill, Maine

MAY THE ROAD RISE WITH YOU

May the road rise with you,
May the wind be ever at your back,
And may the good Lord hold you,
Always in the palm of His hand.

Author Unknown

I MUST NOT HURRY

I must not hurry along this road,

There is so much to see:

A crimson flower, a wrinkled toad,

A knotty, scarred oak tree.

A bubbling brook, a lacy fern,

A cobweb shimmering still;

A yellow bird whose mournful notes

Sound over vale and hill.

Because all nature's loveliness

Is very dear to me,

I must not hurry along this road,

There is too much to see.

Betty Jean Soule
Camp Fire Girl
Kansas City, Missouri

THE NIGHT

No night, not even a winter night, is quite as dark and silent as it seems. Go out and accept the night on its own terms, even now, and it takes on new or long-forgotten meaning. Walk a country road and you can see as well as feel the winter night, light and live in its own proportions.

Starlight is strangely brilliant, once you accept it. The whole sky has its own glow, which silhouettes the trees and hills. It comes to life on a slope of frost-bronzed grass. It is reflected from the frosty trunks of the birches. It is magnified in the roadside pond, ice-silvered to mirror sheen. It almost gleams from a rooftop, and it is reflected from a darkened window. It is a cold, distant light, yet it is light that marks a path through the woods and gives shape and form to roadside walls and rocky banks.

And, though, the insects are gone, the night is not silent. No fox may bark, no owl hoot, and yet the night is alive with sound and movement. The subtle movement and infinitely varied voices of the wind. A leaf scuffs along the road. An oak tree, not yet completely naked, rustles crisply. The grasses sigh. There is soft, intermittent whisper in the high tops of the elms. And the towering hemlocks murmur among themselves with a voice quite different from that of whispering pines.

You walk, and you see and hear, and it is ancient knowledge re-remembering. No night is quite so dark as it seems, once you explore it; no night is without its familiar voices, once you are prepared to listen.

Billie Cooper
New York Times
December, 1952.

NIGHT BREEZE

To sit in the quiet solitude and listen to the
sounds of a night
On an island guarded by moonlight, kept fresh by
a Puget Sound breeze,
Ever so carefully touching the tall madronas'
dry leaves.
Falling crisply like raindrops revealing the
night breeze,
This is life breathing freely from the depths
of eternity's soul.
This is reality which quickens belief in that
which man can't control.
This is what speaks to those who will listen
and find in the sounds of the night
On a Puget Sound Isle, what his heart only
knows is peace and faith in life.

Karen Edler, Counselor
Camp Sealth, 1959

WIND SONG

Why turn your head away from me
and cringe and shiver?
I'm playing for you, don't you see?
My harp the bough of every tree.
Come, sing this joyful melody
Of crystal winter.

Betty Wilcox, Junior Camper
Camp Wabunaki
Douglas Hill, Maine

AT NIGHT

I think the sky is a canopy of blue velvet
O'er spreading the earth,
At night the sun pulls back a canopy
As it goes to rest.
Then we see the mystery of what lies beyond -
A heaven of stars.

Mildred Casey
Camp Fire Director

THE BRIMMING CUP

My forest was a brimming cup of beauty
That through the long lovely months flowed free.
I often drank of purple tinted clouds
Of pine hills cloaked in rain-silvered shrouds.
From gay moon paths across the lake I quaffed
From water lilies with faces that laughed
To know that they had found the sun and sky.
My heart drank the orange warmth of a butterfly,
The cheerful zoom of a frog on a lily pad,
The great deep silence which the dark night had.
My forest gave a brimming cup each day,
And oh, what burning thirst I brought away!

Dorothy Jane Jastram

THE CATHEDRAL OF LIVING TREES

Before the birth of men there lived great trees,
And crystal streams and lovely melodies
Of birds, that later stirred the hearts of men
To sing, and fashion instruments, though crude,
That throbbed and sang 'neath eager hands.
These taught their feet in rhythm to dance,
While love, and flowers rare, Heaven hewed.
Inspired, perhaps, the spoken word,
Perfected, written, through the ages heard.

And while God's children have been led to reach
The greater depths in thought and word and speech
Attain the beckoning heights in unpierced sky,
And gain in science of the land and sea,
They turn with joy to nature, calm of wood,
And know that sanctuary there is good,
Where they are one with the Great Mystery,
Where singing wind in the trees shall seem
As the dear voice of God in dream.

To this Cathedral in the Wood, our Shrine,
Here let us come, O Love Divine;
Pillars alive in benediction bend
In nearness to Thee, Great Mystery,
Nearness to Thee.

Serena Truman Robinson

GOOD COMPANY

Today I have grown taller from walking with the trees,
The seven sister-poplars who go softly in a line;
And I think my heart is whiter for its parley with a star
That trembled out at nightfall and hung above the pine.

The call-note of a redbird from the cedars in the dusk
Woke his happy mate within me to an answer free and fine;
And a sudden angel beckoned from a column of blue smoke.
Lord, who am I that they should stoop --
these holy folk of Thine?

Karle Wilson Baker

DANDELION

O, little soldier with the golden helmet,
What are you guarding on my lawn?
You with your green gun
And your yellow beard
Why do you stand so stiff?
There is only grass to fight.

Hilda Conkling

I'M GLAD

I'm glad the sky is painted blue,
And the earth is painted green,
With such a lot of nice fresh air
All sandwiched in between.

Author Unknown

I MEANT TO DO MY WORK TO-DAY

I meant to do my work to-day -
    But a brown bird sang in the apple tree
And a butterfly flitted across the field,
    And all the leaves were calling to me.

And the wind went sighing over the land,
    Tossing the grasses to and fro,
And a rainbow held out its shining hand -
    So what could I do but laugh and go?

Richard LeGallienne

WANDERLUST

I know not where the white road runs, nor what
    the blue hills are,
But man can have the sun for friend, and for his
    guide a star;
And there's no end of voyaging when once the
    voice is heard,
For the river calls and the road calls, and,
    oh, the call of a bird!
And come I may, but go I must, and if men ask
    you why,
You may put the blame on the stars and the sun,
    and the white road and the sky!

Gerald Gould

SUNSET

"It is almost eight o'clock now and as the sun is setting it makes the most beautiful picture. If I had any artistic tastes I think I'd sit down at Sunset Point and paint a masterpiece.

I think the sun is like a person. I'm sure you don't know what I mean so I'll try to explain. To me the setting sun is like a little child with long golden curls, just as she is going to bed. Usually the little child's hair is combed and curled, her face is washed and her cheeks are like two red roses. Before the little one goes to bed she shines her happiness and merriment upon all; then she quiets down with a picture of contentment written all over her little face. That is what the sun, as it is sinking, reminds me of.

Sometime when you see an exceptionally lovely red and yellow sunset, see if you don't agree with me."

Anne Harris Robinson
(age 14)
Camp Fire Girl Camper

THE THREE PINES

These pines whose tips seem to reach the sky,
Remind me of God whose majesty is so high.
Three pines together so straight they stand,
Make me think of God whose Almighty hand
Can mend a wound or watch by night
Three pines which stand in the face of God's light.

Mary Thompson, Camper
State Teachers College Camp
Cortland, New York

GOD IS EVERYWHERE

I see Him in the sunset
that lights the western sky,
In the tiny little flower
that nods as I pass by.

I find Him in the even' song
that's chanted by the bird,
In the lapping of the waters
on the crystal lake that's heard.

In the fragrance of the scented pine
like incense burning near,
In the stars that follow twilight
I feel His presence near.

In the chirp of the tiny insect
that lives so near the sod,
I find a message so sublime
that speaks to me of God.

God placed these lovely things about,
these messages so rare,
To steal my thoughts away from earth
and lift my soul in prayer.

He made the stars, the sunset,
the birds, the flowers so fair,
That I might see and think of Him
and find Him everywhere.

Author Unknown

SIGNS OF SPRING

The leaves are bursting on the trees,
The lawns are emerald squares of grass,
And every day some bat and ball
Promote the sale of window glass.

Author Unknown

WONDERFUL WORLD

Great, wide, beautiful, wonderful world,
With the wonderful water 'round you curled,
And the wonderful grass upon your breast --
World, you are beautifully dressed!

The wonderful air is over me,
And the wonderful wind is shaking the tree --
It walks in the water, and whirls the mills,
And talks to itself on top of the hills.

You friendly Earth, how far do you go,
With the wheat fields that nod and the rivers
    that flow,
With cities and gardens and cliffs and isles,
And the people upon you for thousands of miles?

William Brighty Rands

NAUGHTY MORNING

The morning pouted through the hours
With sullen look and frown
She snatched some angry little showers
And poured them on the town.

A naughty temper - what a pout,
She stamped her feet in rain!
Yet, now the sun is coming out
She's well behaved again!

Author Unknown

OUT IN THE FIELDS

The little cares that fretted me,
I lost them yesterday
Among the fields above the sea,
Among the winds at play,
Among the lowing of the herds,
The rustling of the trees,
Among the singing of the birds,
The humming of the bees;

The foolish fears of what might happen,
I cast them all away
Among the clover-scented grass,
Among the new-mown hay,
Among the hushing of the corn,
Where drowsy poppies nod,
Where ill thoughts die and good are born,
Out in the fields with God.

Louise Imogen Guiney

NATURE

All those who love Nature, she loves in return, and will richly reward, not perhaps with the good things, as they are commonly called, but with the best things of this world -- not with money and titles, horses and carriages, but with bright and happy thoughts, contentment and peace of mind ....

John Lubbock

I SAW

I saw a surly teamster skidding logs

and chewing snuff,

He smelled of sweat and bunkhouse beds

And spoke a language foul and rough.

I wondered as he wolfed his lunch,

"Can men like this one dream?"

And then I saw him save some crusts

And feed them to his team.

I saw a work-aged farmer living days

too short for rest,

But he mowed around the places

Where the larks had built their nests.

These men who work against the earth

And live by what it brings,

Have learned the kindest code of

life is loving other living things.

Paul Croy

A PRAYER

I feel, dear God, I'd like to pray
About the things I've seen today,
The flowers and trees with heads held high,
The grasses, birds, and blue of sky.
The wonder of it is so fine,
It doesn't seem that it is mine,
The asters, roses, poplars and pine,
Sweet honeysuckle and light columbine.
I've seen some lovely things today.
I feel, dear God, I'd like to pray.

Doris Jane Dix (age 12)
Chicago, Illinois

THE WOMAN WHO LIVES ON THE HILL

The townsfolk call her "Crazy Nell" ...
The woman on the hill;
The children learn to fear her
Because she's strange and still.

They say she must be very queer
To live in such a place,
But once I saw her stoop and kiss
The purple of a pansy's face.

And once I saw her weep because
A bird had a broken wing;
Again I saw her scatter crumbs
To make the warblers sing.

The village wonders why she lives
Where few feet have trod,
But I know what the reason is ...
Because it's close to God.

Frances Cattlett (age 16)
Camp Fire Girl

THE FRIENDLY PINE

When other trees are stripped and bare,
Without a leaf to shield
The furred and feathered citizens
Of windy wood and field,
And frozen snows are drifted deep
The lofty pine extends
A welcome warm to all its cold
And hungry little friends.

The birds among its tasseled boughs
Find shelter from the blast,
When flying crystals cut the air
And skies are overcast,
And there upon it's spicy cones
The squirrels come to dine,
A guest-house open all the year,
Long live the friendly pine!

Author Unknown

SAY THIS OF HER

She loved the evening star and twilight's blue
And all life's gay, inconsequential things.
She found, each moment, miracles anew
And had respect for tiny, feathered wings.
She loved the earth and all that springs therefrom;
Walked by the sea and wondered at the moon.
She loved to brave the elements in storm,
And moved to music, symphony or tune.
No phase of living, great or good or small,
Escaped her interest - lilacs in the spring,
The vivid carnival of leaves in fall
Or little, secret brooks that leap and sing.
Don't pity her that she was never great;
She had the genius to appreciate.

Lee Avert

LOST OCTOBER

There never comes a day like this,
all gold
And shining like a bubble in the sun,
But I recall the afternoon I told
You I'd no time for play; work must be done:
Work must be done, and there the gold day
wasted,
And there the mellowness of earth and sky
And leaf and flower went hour by hour
untasted
For scruples sown to well in such as I!

And there's October's brightness faded,
turning
Her dear enchantment into dull November,
And seething in my brain one question
burning,
Now what can I, now what can I remember
Of work I bent above that day until
It was too late to climb the golden hill!

Author Unknown

THE WIND'S WAY

A white way is the wind's way,
The silver side o' the leaf.
Follow the wind, heart of mine,
Heart of grief.

Wind of the dawn, wind of the dusk,
Winged wings of the day,
Who follows the wind must go,
The wind's way.

Author Unknown

BEAUTY

The beauty of this island
Fairly sets my heart afire.
Ah, that I were a poet
That I may express my ever desire.

But, alas, no talent have I,
I cannot make my words rhyme.
All my ideas are lost
In each ripple of time.

Oh, that I were an artist
A great mural would I paint
Of forest and sky and water.
Dear God, my talents are faint.

If I were given to composing
To put what I feel into song,
I would sing of the mighty waters,
But all of the notes are wrong.

Oh, God, I have no talents
With which to share the joy you give,
Alas, I can do nothing but pray,
"Grant all to know true beauty while they live".

Elizabeth McIntire
Camp Sealth Counselor
1959

SUMMER

Summer by summer...the colorful days
Fall from the world like wilted bouquets;
But safely they leave us, where no one can see,
In the earth all the seeds of the summer to be.

Author Unknown

IN A GREEN GARDEN

I had a silver penny
I brought in town to spend
But passed it to a ragged man
Who walked without a friend.

I cut a flute of willow,
Green willow in the spring,
Then gave it to a crippled child
Who taught it how to sing.

Mine was a heart for loving
As tender as the rain.
I lost it to a whistling boy
Who sailed away to Spain.

I live in a green garden
Where birds sing every day,
But all the things which bring me joy
Are those I gave away.

Beulah May

PRAIRIE

To make a prairie takes a clover and
one bee,
One clover and a bee
And revery.
The revery alone will do
If bees are few.

Author Unknown

. . . of *Faith* and *Inspiration*

THE SILVER CANOE

The pack is too hard on the shoulders,
    The feet are too slow on the trail;
The log that was blazing, but smolders,
    And gone is the zest from the tale.

Then why should wistfully tarry,
    Old comrades, grown feeble and few?
Come, rest on the shore of the carry
    And wait for the Silver Canoe.

The Silver Canoe - and who guesses
    What paddle is plied for the stern?
It comes in the silence that blesses
    Through forests of cedar and fern;

It comes when the twilight is fading
    Through shadow to moonlight and then
It goes with the earth weary-lading
    From moonlight to shadow again.

It glides to a lake in the mountains
    As blue as the skies that are fair
And fed by the purest of fountains,
    A lake of the woodlands; and there,

Oh, pathfinder, cragsman, frontiersman,
    Your cabin is ready for you;
For peace is the goal of the Steersman,
    The bourne of the Silver Canoe.

Arthur Guiterman

REMEMBER THIS

Be good, but not too good - a little naughty,
but not too naughty.
Say a prayer if you feel that way, say
Damn if it gives you consolation.

Be kind to the world always, if possible -
yet, if you must be unkind,
Smash right and left, get it over and
forget it.

Smile, always smile, have a smile ready even though
sometimes it hurts. Grab all the happiness you can -
wherever and whenever you can - don't let even a
wee bit slip past you.
Live, above all things live, don't simply exist.

If you are blessed enough to know what real love is -
love with all your heart, soul, and body.

Live your life so that at any hour you will be able to
shake hands with yourself and try to accomplish at
least one thing worthwhile each day. Then when your
nights come you will be able to pull up the covers and
say to yourself "I have done my best".

F. Collis Wildman

IF

If you can keep your head when all about you
Are losing theirs and blaming it on you,
If you can trust yourself when all men doubt you,
But make allowance for their doubting too;
If you can wait and not be tired by waiting,
Or, being lied about, don't deal in lies,
Or being hated, don't give way to hating,
And yet don't look too good, nor talk too wise;

If you can dream - and not make dreams your master;
If you can think - and not make thoughts your aim;
If you can meet with Triumph and Disaster
And treat those two imposters just the same;
If you can bear to hear the truth you've spoken
Twisted by knaves to make a trap for fools,
Or watch the things you gave your life to, broken,
And stoop and build 'em up with wornout tools;

If you can make one heap of all your winnings
And risk it on one turn of pitch and toss,
And lose, and start at your beginnings
And never breathe a word about your loss;
If you can force your heart and nerve and sinew
To serve your turn long after they are gone,
And so hold on when there is nothing in you
Except the Will which says to them: "Hold on";

If you can talk with crowds and keep your virtue,
Or walk with Kings - nor lose the common touch;
If neither foes nor loving friends can hurt you;
If all men count with you, but none too much;
If you can fill the unforgiving minute
With sixty seconds' worth of distance run -
Yours is the Earth and everything that's in it.
And - which is more - you'll be a Man, my son!

Rudyard Kipling

AN IF FOR GIRLS

If you can dress to make yourself attractive,
And not make puffs and curls your chief delight;
If you can row and swim, be strong and active,
Yet of gentler graces lose not sight;
If you can dance without a craze of dancing,
Play without giving play too strong a hold,
Enjoy the love of a friend without romancing,
Care for the weak, the friendless and the old;

If you can master French and Greek and Latin,
And not acquire as well a priggish mein,
If you can feel the touch of silk and satin,
Without despising calico and jean;
If you can ply a saw and use a hammer,
Can do a man's work when the need occurs,
Can sing when asked without excuse or stammer,
Can rise above unfriendly snubs or slurs;
If you can bake good bread as well as fudges,
Can sew with skill and have an eye for dust,
If you can be a friend and hold no grudges,
A girl whom all can love because they must;

If sometime you should meet and love another,
And make a home with faith and peace enshrined,
And you its soul - a loyal wife and mother -
You'll work out pretty nearly to my mind,
The plan that's been developed through the ages,
And win the best that life can have in store.
You'll be, my girl, a model for the sages -
A woman whom the world will bow before.

Elizabeth Lincoln Otis

HAPPINESS

Happiness, I have discovered, is nearly always a rebound from hard work. It is one of the follies of men to imagine that they can enjoy mere thought, or emotion, or sentiment. As well, try to eat beauty. For happiness must be tricked! She loves to see men at work. She loves sweat, weariness, self-sacrifice. She will be found not in palaces but lurking in cornfields and factories and hovering over littered desks; she crowns the unconscious head of the busy child. If you look up suddenly from hard work you will see her, but if you look too long, she fades sorrowfully away.

There is something fine in hard physical labor. One actually stops thinking. I often work long without any thought whatever, so far as I know, save that in connection with the monotonous repetition of the labor itself - down with the spade, out with it, over with it - and repeat. And, yet, sometimes, mostly in the forenoon when I am not tired at all, I will suddenly have a sense of the world opening around me, a sense of its beauty and meaning, giving me a peculiar deep happiness, that is near complete content.

David Grayson

HAPPINESS

One is happy as a result of one' s own efforts, once one knows the necessary ingredients of happiness-simple tastes, a certain degree of courage, self-denial to a point, love of work, and, above all, a clear conscience. Happiness is no vague dream, of that I now feel certain. By the proper use of experience and thought one can draw much from oneself. By determination and patience one can even restore one' s health. So, let us live life as it is, and not be ungrateful.

George Sand

DROP A STONE INTO THE WATER

Drop a stone into the water-
In a moment it is gone,
But there are a hundred ripples
Circling on and on and on,
Say an unkind word this moment-
In a moment it is gone
But there are a hundred ripples
Circling on and on and on.
Say a word of cheer and splendor-
In a moment it is gone
But there are a hundred ripples
Circling on and on and on.

Author Unknown

HOLD FAST YOUR DREAMS

Hold fast your dreams!
Within your heart
Keep one, still, secret spot
Where dreams may go,
And sheltered so,
May thrive and grow --
Where doubt and fear are not.
O, keep a place apart,
Within your heart,
For little dreams to go!

We see so many ugly things --
Deceits and wrongs and quarrelings,
We know, alas! we know
How quickly fade
The color in the west,
The bloom upon the flower,
The bloom upon the breast
And youth's blind hour.
Yet, keep within your heart
A place apart
Where little dreams may go,
May thrive and grow.
Hold fast -- hold fast your dreams!

Louis Driscoll

THEN LAUGH

Build for yourself a strong box
Fashion each part with care.
When it's strong as your hand can make it,
Put all of your troubles there.

Hide there all your thoughts of failures
And each bitter cup that you quaff,
Lock all your heartaches within it,
Then sit on the lid and laugh.

Tell no one else its contents,
Never its secrets share.
When you've dropped in your care and worry,
Keep them forever there.

Hide them from sight so completely
That the world will never dream half.
Fasten the strong box securely,
Then sit on the lid and laugh.

Author Unknown

A LITTLE DREAM

A little dream keeps house with me
Outside the surge and flow
Of city things, of wind, of sea,
The world the great ones know.

But I am wise, and therefore know,
For sewing up a seam
Or keeping cupboard shelves just so,
There's nothing like a dream.

Author Unknown

I AM GOOD HEALTH

I am the cheapest thing in the world.
With me men have felt within them
the power to move mountains, to fly
the air as birds, to gain the wealth
of Croesus. I am the secret of happiness.
Without me, the years are but a
menace, old age a tragedy.

I offer myself to you, and you do not
heed. I bide my time. Tomorrow you
will come begging, but I will turn
aside. I cannot - I will not -
be ignored.

I am the sunlight of the day, the star-
dotted heaven of the night. I hold
your future within the hollow of my
hand. I can make of you what I will.
I am the door to opportunity, the
open road to fairyland of dreams.

I am the most important thing in the
world, the one without which all
else is impossible.
You ask me who I am and I shall
tell you . . .

I AM GOOD HEALTH.

Author Unknown

I AM COURTESY

I am a little thing with a big meaning
I help everybody
I unlock doors, open hearts, dispel prejudices
I create friendship and good will
I inspire respect and admiration
Everybody loves me
I bore nobody
I violate no law
I cost nothing
Many have praised me, none has condemned me
I am pleasing to those of high and low degree
I am useful every moment of the day
I AM COURTESY.

Author Unknown

VICTORY

He who gains a victory over other men
is strong;
But he who gains a victory over himself
is all powerful.

Lao-tse

NEVER GIVE UP

Never give up! It is wiser and better
Always to hope, than ever despair;
Fling off the load of Doubt's cankering fetter,
And break the dark spell of tyrannical Care.
NEVER GIVE UP or the burdens may sink you;
Providence kindly has mingled the cup,
And in all trials and troubles, bethink you,
The watchword of life must be, "Never give up!"

Martin Farquhar Tupper

A LITTLE SONG OF LIFE

Glad that I live am I,
That the sky is blue,
Glad for the country lanes,
And the fall of dew.

After the sun the rain,
After the rain the sun;
This is the way of life,
Till the work be done.

All that we need to do,
Be we low or high,
Is to see that we grow
Nearer the sky.

Lizette Woodworth Reese

THE WINDS OF FATE

One ship drives east, another west,
With the selfsame winds that blow.
'Tis the set of the sail not the gales,
That determines the way they go.

Like the winds of the sea are the ways of Fate
As we voyage thru life.
'Tis the set of the soul that decides its goal,
And not the calm or the strife.

Ella Wheeler Wilcox

THE TWENTY THIRD PSALM
THE AMERICAN INDIAN VERSION

The Great Father above is the Shepherd
Chief. I want not. He throws out to me
a rope, and the name of the rope is Love.

And He draws me. He draws me to where the
grass is green and the water is not dangerous.
And I eat and lie down satisfied.

Sometimes my heart is very weak. And falls down,
but He lifts it up again and draws me into a
good road.

His name is Wonderful.

Sometime - it may be very soon - it may be
longer - it may be a long, long time. He will
draw me into a place between the mountains. It
is dark there but I'll not draw back. I'll be
afraid not.

For it is there between the mountains that the
Shepherd Chief will be.

And the hunger I have felt in my heart all
through life will be satisfied.

Sometimes He makes the love rope into a whip.
But afterwards He gives me a staff to lean on.

He spreads a table before me with all kinds of food.

He puts His hands upon my head, and all the
'tired' is gone.

My cup He fills till it runs over.

What I tell you is true. I lie not. These roads
that are a way ahead will stay with me through this
life. And afterwards I will go to live in the Big
Tepee and sit down with the Shepherd Chief forever.

Author Unknown

I GIVE THEE THANKS

Again, O God, I give thanks for these:
For song and symphony,
For age-long quest of truth,
For minds full grown that would not play in shallow pools,
For mariners that launched their barks toward unknown seas,
For prophets crying in a desert waste
Unheard till lifted on a cross they drew men near,
For all the great who dipped their pens in gold
And wrote in deathless words the deeps of life,
For humble folk who died unheralded
And left the world enriched by wealth of love,
For these, O God, I thank Thee.

Again, O God, I give Thee thanks for these:
For friends who understand,
For useful work, and laughter lightening toil,
For comradeship with youth, alive to know and do,
For mellowed age,
For homes where happy children's voices sound,
For hearths where lambent flames play merrily,
For tables spread with daily sustenance,
And couches that give rest when day is done . . .
For these, O God, I thank Thee.

I give Thee thanks, O God,
For these thy gifts unbought with coin:
For the beauty of the earth and sky,
For goodly heritage,
For life and love and fellowship,
For that great Gift, surpassing all,
The gift of Thine own Life to men.
For these, O God, I give Thee thanks,
And lift my hymn of praise to Thee.

Georgia Harkness

A CREED FOR THOSE WHO HAVE SUFFERED

I asked God for strength, that I might
achieve.
I was made weak, that I might learn to
humbly obey...
I asked for health, that I might do greater
things.
I was given infirmity, that I might do better
things.
I asked for riches, that I might be happy.
I was given poverty, that I might be wise.
I asked for power, that I might have the
praise of men.
I was given weakness, that I might feel
the need of God.
I asked for all things that I might enjoy life.
I was given life that I might enjoy all things.
I got nothing that I asked for - but everything
I had hoped for.
Almost despite myself, my unspoken prayers
were answered.
I am among men, all men, most richly
blessed.

Written by an Unknown
Confederate Soldier

INVICTUS

Out of the night that covers me,
Black as the pit from pole to pole,
I thank whatever Gods may be
For my unconquerable soul.

It matters not how strait the gate,
How charged with punishments the scroll,
I am the master of my fate;
I am the captain of my soul.

W. E. Henley

SLOW ME DOWN, LORD

Give me, amidst the confusion of my day, the calmness of the everlasting hills. Break the tension of my nerves and muscles with the soothing music of the singing streams that live in my memory. Help me to know the restorative power of sleep. Teach me the art of taking minute vacations -- of slowing down to look at a flower, to chat with a friend, to pat a dog, to read a few lines from a good book.

Remind me each day of the fable of the hare and the tortoise, that I may know the race is not always to the swift; that there is more in life than increasing its speed. Let me look upward to the branches of the towering oak, and know that it grew slowly and well.

Slow me down, Lord, and inspire me to send my roots deep into the soil of life's enduring values, that I may grow toward the stars of my greater destiny. Amen.

L. O. Crain

PERSISTENCE

Nothing in the world can take the place of persistence. Talent will not; nothing is more common than unsuccessful men with talent. Genius will not; unrewarded genius is almost a proverb. Education will not; the world is full of educated derelicts. Persistence and determination are omnipotent. The slogan "Press on" has solved and always will solve the problems of the human race.

Calvin Coolidge

FATHER IN HEAVEN

For flowers that bloom about our feet,
For tender grass so fresh, so sweet,
For song of bird and hum of bee,
For all things fair we hear or see,
Father in Heaven, we thank Thee!

For blue of stream and blue of sky,
For pleasant shade of branches high,
For fragrant air and cooling breeze,
For beauty of the blooming trees,
Father in Heaven, we thank Thee!

For mother-love and father-care,
For brothers strong and sisters fair,
For love at home and here each day,
For guidance, lest we go astray,
Father in Heaven, we thank Thee!

For this new morning with its light,
For rest and shelter of the night,
For health and food, for love and friends,
For everything His goodness sends,
Father in Heaven, we thank Thee!

Author Unknown

WELL, MY HEART, WE HAVE BEEN HAPPY

Well, my heart, we have been happy.
Let us snatch that from the wreck of things.
But when the forest is choked with ashes,
While still the flame around its old nest flashes --
'Tis a brave bird sits on a charred limb --
And sings.

Author Unknown

BE THE BEST OF WHATEVER YOU ARE

If you can't be a pine on the top of the hill,
Be a scrub in the valley, --- but, be
The best little scrub by the side of the hill,
Be a bush if you can't be a tree.

If you can't be a bush, be a bit of grass,
And some highway some happier make,
If you can't be a muskie, then just be a bass -
But be the liveliest bass in the lake.

If you can't be a highway, then just be a trail,
If you can't be the sun, be a star;
It isn't by size that you win or you fail,
Be the best of whatever you are.

Douglas Malloch

TO BE WHAT WE ARE

To be what we are, and to become what we are capable of becoming, it is the only end of life.

Robert Louis Stevenson

THE TOWN OF DON'T-YOU-WORRY

There's a town called Don't-You-Worry,
On the banks of River Smile;
Where the Cheer-Up and Be-Happy
Blossom sweetly all the while.
Where the Never-Grumble flower
Blooms beside the fragrant Try,
And the Ne'er-Give-Up and Patience
Point their faces to the sky.

In the valley of Contentment,
In the province of I-Will,
You will find this lovely city,
At the foot of No-Fret Hill.
There are thoroughfares delightful
In this very charming town,
And on every hand are shade trees
Named the Very-Seldom-Frown.

Rustic benches quite enticing
You'll find scattered here and there;
And to each a vine is clinging
Called the Frequent-Earnest-Prayer.
Everybody there is happy
And is singing all the while,
In the town of Don't-You-Worry,
On the banks of River Smile.

I. J. Bartlett

THE HALFWAY HOUSE OF LITTLE THINGS

There's a halfway house of little things
That stands on the mountain of life.
It's just when you get too tired to climb
That this little house comes into sight.

The refreshing cup is a lovely word
Or the pressure of a hand.
And you rest for awhile in a loving smile
That gives you the strength to stand.

You had thought you'd turn on the downward way
For the road was so rough and steep.
But there at the halfway house you caught
The glimpse of the sunlight peak.

Though small is this house of a kindly word
Or the touch of a friendly hand,
We shall know when we reach the summit
It is part of his own great plan.

Jennie T. Sheperd

A FILLER

Resolutions, evolutions, for a little while
Then remorse, for recourse,
To our former style.

But to strive, tho' not arrive
To a higher goal,
Is the brewer and renewer
Of Life's better bowl.

Philip H. Welch

BLIND

"Show me your God!", the doubter cries.
I point him to the smiling skies;
I show him the woodland greens;
I show him the peaceful sylvan scenes;
I show him the winter swans and frost;
I show him the waters tempest-tost;
I show him the hills rock-ribbed and strong;
I bid him hear the thrush's song;
I show him flowers in the close -
The lily, violet, and rose;
I show him rivers, babbling streams;
I show him youthful hopes and dreams;
I show him maids with eager hearts;
I show him toilers in the marts;
I show him stars, the moon, the sun;
I show him deeds of kindness done;
I show him joy, I show him care,
And still he holds his doubting air,
And faithless goes his way, for he
Is blind of soul and cannot see!

John Kendrick Bangs

LOOK UP

Look up and not down.
Look forward and not back.
Look out and not in.
Lend a hand.

Edward Everett Hale

THE SACRAMENT OF WORK

Upon thy bended knees thank God for work, -
Work - once man's penance, now his high reward!
For work to do and strength to do the work,
We thank Thee, Lord!

Since outcast Adam toiled to make a home,
The primal curse a blessing has become,
Man in his toil finds recompense for loss,
A workless world had known nor Christ nor Cross.

Some toil for love, and some for simple greed,
Some reap a harvest past their utmost need,
More, in their less find truer happiness,
And all, in work, relief from bitterness.

A toiler with his hands was God's own Son;
Like His, to Him be all thy work well done.
None so forlorn as he that hath no work,
None so abject as he that work doth shirk.

Upon thy bended knees, thank God for work!
In workless days all ills and evil lurk;
For work to do, and strength to do the work,
We thank Thee, Lord.

John Oxenham

ALWAYS FINISH

If a task is once begun
Never leave it till it's done.
Be the labor great or small,
Do it well or not at all.

Author Unknown

IT COULDN'T BE DONE

Somebody said that it couldn't be done,
    But he with a chuckle replied
That maybe it couldn't, but he would be one
    Who wouldn't say so till he'd tried.
So he buckled right in, with a trace of a grin
    On his face. If he worried he hid it.
He started to sing as he tackled the thing
    That couldn't be done, and he did it.

Somebody scoffed: "Oh, you'll never do that;
    At least no one ever had done it".
But he took off his coat and he took off his hat,
    And the first thing we knew he'd begun it.
With a lift of his chin and a bit of a grin,
    Without fear and doubting and quiddit,
He started to sing as he tackled the thing
    That couldn't be done, and he did it.

Edgar A. Guest

WHICH

Isn't it strange that princes and kings,
And clowns who caper in sawdust rings,
And common folk like you and me,
Are builders of eternity?

To each is given a bag of tools,
A shapeless mass, a book of rules;
And each must make, ere his life has flown,
A stumbling block, or a stepping stone.

Cale Young Rice

THE VICTOR

If you think you are beaten, you are;
If you think you dare not, you don't.
If you'd like to win, but think you can't,
It's almost a cinch you won't.

If you'll think you'll lose, you're lost,
For out in the world we find
Success begins with a fellow's will;
It's all in the state of mind.

Life's battles don't always go
To the stronger or faster man;
But soon or late the man who wins
Is the one who thinks he can.

C. W. Longenecker

MY CROWN

My crown is in my heart, not on my head;
Not deck'd with diamonds and Indian stones,
Nor to be seen: my crown is called content.

William Shakespeare

TRUTH NEVER DIES

Truth never dies. The ages come and go.
The mountains wear away, the stars retire.
Destruction lays the earth's mighty cities low;
And empires, states and dynasties expire;
But caught and handled onward by the wise,
TRUTH NEVER DIES.

Author Unknown

TO THE MEN WHO LOSE

Here's to the men who lose!
What though their work be e'er so nobly planned,
And watched with zealous care,
No glorious halo crowns their efforts grand;
Contempt is failure's. share.

Here's to the men who lose!
If triumph's easy smile our struggles greet,
Courage is easy then;
The king is he who, after fierce defeat,
Can up and fight again.

Here's to the men who lose!
The ready plaudits of a fawning world
Ring sweet in victor's ears;
The vanquished's banners never are unfurled;
For them sound no cheers.

Here's to the men who lose!
The touchstone of the true worth is not success;
There is a higher test -
Though fate may darkly frown, onward to press,
And bravely do one's best.

Here's to the men who lose!
It is the vanquished's praises that I sing,
And this is the toast I choose:
"A hard fought failure is a noble thing!
Here's to the men who lose!"

George L. Scaraborough

A PRAYER

Lord, let me live like a Regular Man,
With Regular friends and true;
Let me play the game on a Regular plan,
And play it that way all through;
Let me win or lose with a Regular smile
And never be known to whine,
For that is a Regular Fellow's style
And I want to make it mine!

Oh, give me the Regular chance in life,
The same as the rest I pray,
And give me a Regular girl for wife,
To help me along the way;
Let us know the lot of humanity,
Its Regular woes and joys,
And raise a Regular family
Of Regular girls and boys!

Let me live to a Regular good old age,
With Regular snow-white hair,
Having done my labor and earned my wage
And played my game for fair;
And so at last when people scan
My face on its peaceful bier,
They'll say, "Well, he was a Regular Man!"
And drop a Regular tear!

Berton Braley

THE OPTIMIST

The optimist fell ten stories,
At each window bar
He shouted to his friends:
"All right so far."

Author Unknown

I WOULD LIVE MY LIFE

I would live my life as the growing oak
That reaches for stars and sun,
And meets its death with a lightening stroke
When it's growing time is done.

I would live my life as a forest fire
That warms the earth and sky
And takes its way with a wild desire
Up the mountains steep and high.

I would live my life as a turgid stream
That blends with the breathing sea
And mingle my soul and love and dream
With God's infinity.

Author Unknown

SUCCESS

He has achieved success who has lived well, laughed often and loved much; who has gained the respect of intelligent men and the love of little children; who has filled his niche and accomplished his task; who has left the world better than he found it, whether by an improved poppy, a perfect poem or a rescued soul; who has never lacked appreciation of earth's beauty or failed to express it; who has looked for the best in others and given the best he had; whose life was an inspiration; whose memory is a benediction.

Mrs. A. J. Stanley

THE VOICE OF GOD

I sought to hear the voice of God,
And climbed the topmost steeple.
But God declared, "Go down again,
I dwell among the people."

Louis L. Newman

THE COIN

Into my heart's treasury I slipped a coin,
That time cannot take or thief purloin,
Oh, better than the minting of a gold crowned king,
Is the safe kept memory of a lovely thing.

Sara Teasdale

I HAD NO SHOES

I had no shoes and complained
Until I met a man who had no feet.

Sara Cleghorn

AND THESE WORDS WERE CARVED OVER HIS MANTLE

"I am an old man and have had many troubles,
But most of them never happened."

When the world seems dark and
You seem to see trouble ahead -
Read the above.

Author Unknown

WORK

Let me but do my work from day to day,
In field or forest, at the desk or loom,
In roaring market-place or tranquil room;
Let me but find it in my heart to say,
When vagrant wishes beckon me astray,
"This is my work; my blessing, not my doom!
Of all who live, I am the one by whom
This work can best be done in the right way."

Then shall I see it not too great, not small,
To suit my spirit and to prove my powers;
Then shall I cheerful greet the labouring hours,
And cheerful turn, when the long shadows fall
At eventide, to play and love and rest,
Because I know for me my work is best.

Henry Van Dyke

THANK GOD FOR WORK

Thank God for Work,
For peace of ordered lives and busy days,
And happy resting after work well done.

Thank God for Health,
For sunshine warm, for water cool,
For all that ushers in with joy each newborn day.

Thank God for Love,
For homes to which its nameless beauty brings,
The calm content of haven after storm.

Bessie F. Loomis

TAKE TIME TO LIVE

Take time to work,
It is the price of success.
Take time to think,
It is the source of power.
Take time to play,
It is the secret of youth.
Take time to read,
It is the foundation of wisdom.
Take time to be friendly,
It is the road to happiness.
Take time to dream,
It is hitching your wagon to a star.
Take time to love and be loved,
It is the privilege of the gods.
Take time to look around,
It is too short a day to be selfish.
Take time to laugh,
It is the music of the soul.

Author Unknown

THE PAST

The past is the one thing you can't do anything about. The present, - the present's the clay in the sculptor hand; the future's his dream of a masterpiece. But the past's set firmly in stone, or bronze, or marble. It faces you down. It's exactly as you made it.

Author Unknown

LIFE OWES ME NOTHING

Life owes me nothing. Let the years
Bring clouds or azure, joy or tears;
    Already a full cup I've quaffed;
    Already wept and loved and laughed,
And seen in ever-endless ways,
New beauties overwhelm the days.

Life owes me naught. No pain that waits
Can steal the wealth from memory's gates;
    No aftermath or anguish slow
    Can quench the soul fire's early glow.
I breathe, exulting, each new breath,
Embracing Life, ignoring Death.

Life owes me nothing. One clear morn
Is boon enough for being born;
    And be it ninety years or ten,
    No need for me to question when.
While Life is mine, I'll find it good,
And greet each hour with gratitude.

Author Unknown

JOY

To have joy, you must share it,
Happiness was born with a twin.

Author Unknown

THREE GATES

If you are tempted to reveal
A tale to you someone has told
About another, make it pass,
Before you speak, three gates of gold.
These narrow gates: First, "Is it true?"
Then, "Is it needful?" In your mind
Give the truthful answer. And the next
Is the last and narrowest, "Is it kind?"
And if to reach your lips at last
It passes through these gateways three,
Then you may tell the tale, nor fear,
What the result of speech may be.

Beth Day

OUR LIPS AND EARS

If you your lips would keep from slips,
Five things observe with care:
Of whom you speak, to whom you speak,
And how and when and where.

If you your ears would save from jeers,
These things keep mildly hid:
Myself and I, and mine and my,
And how I do and did.

Author Unknown

THE FAIRIES

The fairies have never a penny to spend,
    They haven't a thing put by;
But theirs is the dower of bird and of flower,
    And theirs are the earth and the sky.
And though you may live in a palace of gold
    Or sleep in a dried up ditch,
You could never be poor as the fairies are,
    And never as rich.

Since ever and ever the world began,
    They have danced like a ribbon of flame,
They have sung their song through the centuries
    long,
    And yet it is never the same.
And though you be foolish and though you be wise,
    With hair of silver or gold,
You could never be young as the fairies are,
    And never as old.

Rose Fyleman

JOY

Joy is not a thing you see,
It is what you feel when you watch
        waves breaking
Or when you peer through a net of
        woven violet stems in spring grass.
It is not sunlight, not moonlight
But a separate shining.
Joy lives behind people's eyes.

Hilda Conkling

I JUST WONDER

I just wonder, God,
If sometimes You don't tire
Of comforting other people's woes,
Of listening to their trouble, and
On hearing to their sorrow, say,
"Why did I do that?
Why did I make the great troublesome world?"
God, I sometimes wonder.

God, I sometimes wonder,
If You don't get bored
By the wants of us poor fools on earth.
Don't You rebel at hearing
The foolish things we ask for,
Money, power, strength?
God, I sometimes wonder.

God, I sometimes wonder
Couldn't You ever take some time off,
And just lay Your head in one of the angel's laps,
And let her rub it,
And tell her some of Your troubles?
I think it would help.
God, I just wonder. . . .

Lida Walker (age 14)
Atlanta, Georgia

AN OLD INDIAN PRAYER

Oh, Thou Great Spirit,
As I close mine eyes in slumber tonight
Have I done enough today
To earn the right to live to-morrow?

Author Unknown

MY SYMPHONY

To live content with small means; to seek elegance rather than luxury; and refinement rather than fashion; to be worthy, not respectable; and wealthy, not rich; to study hard, think quietly, talk gently, act frankly; to listen to stars and birds, to babes and sages, with open hearts; to bear all cheerfully, do all bravely, await occasions, hurry never. In a word, to let the spiritual, unbidden and unconscious, grow up through the common. This is to be my symphony.

William Henry Channing

POETRY

One is sometimes inclined to forget that poetry is everywhere - in concrete, in steel, in basalt, in the thousand materials with which we try to bind our souls to the dust. But each of us will write one poem - and we shall make it of the earth's most intractable materials, our own refractory heart's.

Author Unknown

GIVE ME A HILL TO CLIMB

Give me a stony road
And strength for wayfaring;
Give me a storm to dare
And joy in daring;

Give me a battle to win
And courage to fight;
Give me a hill to climb
And strength to gain in height;

And when I reach its sumit
One thing I'll ask of Thee;
Give me a hill beyond
Calling aloud to me.

Gertrude Bridges

IDEALS

Ideals are like stars; you will not succeed in touching them with your hands, but like the seafaring man on the desert of waters, you choose them as your guides, and following them, you reach your destiny, unfailing all.

Carl Schurz

SOUL LAUNDRY

Now I lay me down to sleep
And pray the Lord my soul to keep,
Mend the places that are worn,
Remove the spots, repair the torn.

Return to me with coming light,
I pray that I can keep it bright,
That tomorrow night with face a-beaming,
I can say, "Just press it God without
the cleaning".

Jean Eisenstein (age 16)
Camp Fire Girl

THE WAYS

To every man there openeth
A Way, a Ways, and a Way,
And the High Soul climbs the High Way,
And the Low Soul gropes the Low,
And in between, on the misty flats,
The rest drift to and fro.
But to every man there openeth
A High Way and a Low.
And every man decideth
The Way his soul shall go.

John Oxenham

AN ANCIENT PRAYER

Give me a good digestion, Lord, and also something
to digest;
Give me a healthy body, Lord, and sense to keep it
at its best.
Give me a healthy mind, good Lord, to keep the
good and pure in sight,
Which seeing sin, is not appalled, but finds a
way to set it right.

Give me a mind that is not bound, that does not
whimper, whine or sigh.
Don't let me worry overmuch about the fussy thing
called I.
Give me a sense of humor, Lord; give me the grace
to see a joke,
To get some happiness from life and pass it on
to other folk.

Thomas H. B. Webb

MY DAYS

My days are full of blunders,
Oh, how I've always yearned
To live one life for practice . . .
Another when I've learned.

Author Unknown

HAPPINESS

Happiness is a halfway station between too much and too little.

Author Unknown

CANDLE DIPPING

A candle's but a simple thing,
It starts with just a bit of string;
Yet dipped and dipped with patient hand,
It gathers wax upon the strand
Until, complete and snowy white,
It gives at last a lovely light.

Life seems so like that bit of string;
Each deed we do, a simple thing.
Yet day by day on life's strand
We work with patient heart and hand,
It gathers joy, makes dark days bright,
And gives at last a lovely light.

Author Unknown

LEARNING

Hope it was that tutored me
And love that taught me more.
And now I learn at sorrow's knee,
The self same lore.

Author Unknown

PERFECT BLISS

Three things I have for perfect bliss,
No further need I look;
An open fire burning bright,
An apple, and a book.

Author Unknown

HE WHO KNOWS

He who knows not, and knows not that he knows
not, is a fool, shun him;
He who knows not, and knows that he knows not,
is a child, teach him.
He who knows, and knows not that he knows,
is asleep, wake him.
He who knows, and knows that he knows, is
wise, follow him.

Persian Proverb

A WISE OLD OWL

A wise old owl lived in an oak;
The more he saw the less he spoke;
The less he spoke the more he heard;
Why can't we all be like that bird?

Edward Heresy Richards

LOOK

Do not look for wrong and evil ---
You will find them if you do;
As you measure for your neighbor,
He will measure back to you.
Look for goodness, look for gladness ---
You will meet them all the while;
If you bring a smiling visage
To the glass, you will meet a smile.

Author Unknown

A SMILE

Let others cheer the winning man,
There's one I hold worthwhile;
'Tis he who does the best he can,
Then loses with a smile.
Beaten he is, but not to stay
Down with the rank and file;
That man will win some other day,
Who loses with a smile.

Author Unknown

A CHIP ON HIS SHOULDER

He always has something to grumble about,
    Has the man with a chip on his shoulder;
The world to the dogs is going, no doubt,
    To the man with a chip on his shoulder;
The clouds are too dark, the sun is too bright.
    No matter what happens, it is never right;
When peace is prevailing he is spoiling to fight,
    The man with a chip on his shoulder.

Author Unknown

MEASURE

When I measure myself by the grasses,
I find I am very tall.
When I measure by the mountains,
I do not exist at all.

Author Unknown

LIGHT

The night has a thousand eyes,
The day but one;
Yet, the light of the bright world dies
With the dying sun.

The mind has a thousand eyes,
And the heart but one;
Yet, the light of a whole life dies
When its love is done.

Francis W. Bourdillon

LOST . . . FOREVER

Lost, yesterday somewhere
between sunrise and sunset, two golden
hours, each set with sixty diamond
minutes. No reward is offered for
they are gone forever.

Horace Mann

LESSON

They who have learned the way to live,
Plant wisely, though they may not reap;
And this is well, since what we give
Is all that we may get to keep.

Margaret E. Bruner

MORNING PRAYER

Take a little dash of cold water,
A little leaven of prayer,
A little bit of sunshine gold
Dissolved in morning air.

Add to your meal some merriment,
A thought for kith and kin.
And, then as the prime ingredient,
Plenty of work thrown in.

Flavor it all with the essence of love.
Let a good old book
And a glance above
Complete a well-spent day.

Author Unknown

AGE

Age is a quality of mind.
If you have left your dreams behind,
If hope is cold,
If you no longer look ahead,
If your ambitions' fires are dead,
Then you are old.

But if from life you take the best,
And in your life you keep the jest,
If love you hold;
No matter how the years go by,
No matter how the birthdays fly,
You are not old.

Author Unknown

CAMP PRAYER

Dear Lord, as once again we gather here
In this thy temple, fragrant, green, and still,
Open our eyes, we pray Thee, to the beauty
Surrounding us in sky and lake and hill.
May memories of the sun and moon and starlight
Come thronging when the winter nights are chill.

Let us find beauty, too, in other things...
In lives of those around us every day;
In friendship, and in hearts made glad with
giving,
In laughter and good cheer, in children's play.
And may we keep some beauty always with us
To share with others all along the way.

Elizabeth Bowie
Senior Camper, July, 1940
Camp Wabunaki
Douglas Hill, Maine

HE WHO LIVES...

He who lives with his own child lives
with Nature;
He who lives with another's child lives
with God.

Author Unknown

WHATEVER YOU ARE

Whatever you are by nature, keep to it; never desert your line of talent. Be what nature intended you for, and you will succeed; be anything else, and you will be ten thousand times worse than nothing.

Sydney Smith

A CAMP PRAYER

Dear Lord, beside another lake
The little children come to Thee
Here suffer is to come and take
The lessons taught in Galilee.

When in gray dawns beneath our trees
We watch the darting wings above
We know the Lord who cares for these
Has given us a greater love.

Below us lie the waters clear
Steel gray, unsullied, cooling, still,
Lord, as we cleanse our bodies here
Cleanse Thou our hearts from every ill.

We thank Thee for our pleasant bread,
This spacious room with sunshine rife.
Of all our house be Thou the head
And give to us the bread of life.

Thou lovedst to see the children play
Together in the market-place.
Let all our games, each joyous day,
Be friendly, as before Thy face.

And when at dusk the thrushes call
And through dark pines the stars appear
Send Thou the peace that passeth all
Upon Thy sleeping children here.

Pierson Curtis, Counselor
Camp Wabunaki
Douglas Hill, Maine

A PRAYER

Lord, Thou knowest better than I know myself that
I am growing older, and will someday be old.
Keep me from getting talkative, and particularly
from the fatal habit of thinking I must say something on every subject and on every occasion.
Release me from craving to try to straighten out
everybody's affairs.
Keep my mind free from the recital of endless
details . . . give me wings to get to the point.
I ask for grace enough to listen to the tales of
other's pains. Help me to endure with patience.
But seal my lips on my own aches and pains - they
are increasing and my love of rehearsing them
is becoming sweeter as the years go by.
Teach me the glorious lesson that occasionally it
is possible that I may be mistaken.
Keep me reasonably sweet; I do not want to be a
saint - some of them are hard to live with -
but a sour old woman is one of the crowning
works of the devil.
Make me thoughtful, but not moody; helpful, but
not bossy. With my vast store of wisdom, it
seems a pity not to use it all - but Thou
knowest, Lord, that I want a few friends at the
end.

A favorite of former
Gov. Thomas E. Dewey.
Written by a Mother Superior
who wished to remain
anonymous.

LOOKING GLASS

The world is a looking-glass, and gives back to every man the reflection of his own face. Frown at it, and it in turn will look sourly upon you; laugh at it and with it, and it is a jolly, kind companion.

William M. Thackeray

A SIMPLE PRAYER

Lord, make me an instrument of your peace!
Where there is hatred, let me sow love;
Where there is injury, pardon;
Where there is doubt, faith;
Where there is despair, hope;
Where there is darkness, light;
Where there is sadness, joy.
O Divine Master, grant that
I may not so much seek
To be consoled as to console;
To be understood as to understand;
To be loved as to love;
For it is in giving that we receive;
It is in pardoning that we are pardoned;
And it is in dying that we are born to
eternal life.
Amen

St. Francis of Assisi

A PRAYER

Heavenly Father,
Convince the hearts of all of us that
if we build in wood, it will some day rot;
if we build in marble, it is destined to crumble
before the onslaughts of time;
if we build in steel, it will someday flow as
water before the melting process of the
universe.
But if we build in human character,
If we build usefulness, devotion, honor and integrity
in the lives of our youth,
We build for eternity.

Dr. Julius Mark

A PRAYER

Help me, God. Give me the courage, the inspiration and the force to do it myself. But, too, give me the little push I need when all seems too great for me to exist. Force me to look into the eyes of temptation and be able to turn and walk away. Fill my heart with the joy of living, the peace towards all, a smile to all I pass, condolence to the sorrowful, and life to the destitute.

And, Father, when I ask for too much, show me the sick, the naked, and homeless. Show me the lame and mutilated. And after I've seen, show me the way to give, the way life is to be.

I guess, Father, my soul has spoken all that was waiting for your ears only. And, yet, teach me to be humble. Oh, my Lord, teach me to pray. Amen.

Nancy Legett
Camp Sealth Counselor
August, 1958

HOLD FAST

In the bitter waves of woe
Beaten and tossed about,
By the sullen winds that blow
From the desolate shores of doubt
Where the anchors that faith has cast
Are dragging in the gale,
I am quietly holding fast
To the things that cannot fail.

Author Unknown

A CAMPER'S PRAYER

"Our Father, Creator of the visible beauty of all nature, we bring to Thee now our grateful remembrance of that countryside which is particularly precious to each of us, as we pause to recall those little landscapes where our spirits have been restored; where Thy peace and tranquility have calmed us -- perhaps in the quiet handclapping of green leaves, the reflection of Thy vast sky in a still pool, the immovable glory of Thy high hills, the leashed splendor of Thy mighty deep. Help us to think Thy thoughts, whether in memory of those loved spots or in actual contact with Thy earth, that Thy touch may heal us and Thy beauty be upon us, O God."

Author Unknown
From "The Hitching Post"
Western Pennsylvania Section
of the American Camping
Association, September, 1963.

LIFE'S RECIPE

1 cup of good thoughts
1 cup of kind deeds
1 cup of consideration for others
2 cups of sacrifice for others
3 cups of forgiveness
2 cups of well-beaten faults

Mix these thoroughly and add tears of joy and sorrow and sympathy for others. Fold in 4 cups of prayer and faith to lighten the ingredients and raise the texture to great height of Christian living. After pouring all this into your daily life, bake well with the heat of human kindness. Serve with a smile.

Given to Marilyn Greifzu
by her Grandmother

...of Friendship

THIS IS FRIENDSHIP

I love you, not only for what you are, but for what I am when I am with you.

I love you, not only for what you have made of yourself, but for what you are making of me.

I love you for the part of me that you bring out.

I love you for putting your hand into my heaped-up heart and passing over all the frivolous and weak things that you cannot help seeing there, and drawing into the light all the beautiful, radiant things that no one else has looked quite far enough to find.

I love you for ignoring the possibilities of the fool in me and for laying firm hold of the possibilities of good in me.

I love you for closing your eyes to the discords in me, and adding to the music in me by worshipful listening.

I love you because you are helping me to make of the lumber of my life, not a tavern, but a temple, and of the words of my days, not a reproach, but a song.

I love you because you have done more than any creed could have done to make me happy.

You could have done it without a touch, without a word, without a sign.

You have done it by being yourself.

After all, perhaps this is what being a friend means.

Mary Carolyn Davies

A GOOD FRIEND

To have a good friend is one of the highest delights of life; to be a good friend is one of the noblest and most difficult undertakings. Friendship depends not upon fancy, imagination or sentiment, but upon character. There is no man so poor that he is not rich if he have a friend; there is no man so rich that he is not poor without a friend. But friendship is a word made to cover many kindly, impermanent relationships. Real friendship is abiding. Like charity, it suffereth long and is kind. Like love, it vaunteth not itself, but pursues the even tenor of its way, unaffrighted by ill-report, loyal in adversity, the solvent of infelicity, the shining jewel of happy days. Friendship has not the irridescent joys of love, though it is closer than is often known to the highest, truest love. Its heights are ever serene, its valleys know few clouds. To aspire to friendship one must cultivate a capacity for faithful affection, a beautiful disinterestedness, a clear discernment. Friendship is a gift, but it is also an acquirement. It is like the rope which the climbers in the high mountains bind themselves for safety, and only a coward cuts the rope when a comrade is in danger. From Cicero to Emerson, and long before Cicero, and forever after Emerson, the praises of friendship have been set forth. Even fragments of friendship are precious and to be treasured. But to have a whole real friend is the greatest of earth gifts save one. To be a whole, real friend is worthy of high endeavor, for faith, truth, courage, and loyalty bring one close to the Kingdom of Heaven.

By Atmos

A PRAYER FOR EVERYDAY

Make me too brave to lie and be unkind.
Make me too understanding, too, to mind
The little hurts companions give, and friends,
The careless hurts that no one quite intends.
Make me too thoughtful to hurt others so.
Help me to know
The inmost hearts of those for whom I care,
Their secret wishes, all loads they bear,
That I may add courage to their own.
May I make lonely folks feel less alone,
And happier ones a little happier yet.
May I forget
What ought to be forgotten; and recall,
That which ought to be recalled, each kindly thing,
Forgetting what might sting.
To all upon my way,
Day after day,
Let me be joy, be hope! Let my life sing!

Mary Carolyn Davies

A CREED

There is a Destiny that makes us brothers,
No one goes his way alone,
All that we give into the lives of others
Comes back into our own.

Edwin Markham

LIFE'S MIRROR

There are loyal hearts, there are spirits brave,
There are souls that are pure and true;
Then give to the world the best you have,
And the best will come back to you.

Give love, and love to your life will flow,
A strength in your utmost need;
Have faith, and a score of hearts will show
Their faith in your word and deed.

Give truth, and your gift will be paid in kind,
And honor will honor meet;
And a smile that is sweet will surely find
A smile that is just as sweet.

Give pity and sorrow to those who mourn,
You will gather in flowers again;
The scattered seeds from your thought outbourne,
Though the sowing seemed in vain.

For life is the mirror of king and slave,
'Tis just what we are and do;
Then give to the world the best you have,
And the best will come back to you.

Madelaine S. Bridges

A PRAYER FOR TODAY

Let me be a little kinder,
Let me be a little blinder,
To the faults of those about me.
Let me praise a little more,
Let me be, when I am weary,
Just a little bit more cheery.
Let me serve a little better.
Let me be a little braver
When temptation bids me waver.
Let me strive a little harder
To be all that I should be.
Let me be a little meeker
With the brother who is weaker.
Let me think more of my neighbor
And a little less of me.

Author Unknown

NOT IN VAIN

If I can stop one heart from breaking,
I shall not live in vain;
If I can ease one life from aching,
Or cool one pain,
Or help one fainting robin
Unto his nest again,
I shall not live in vain.

Emily Dickinson

THE BRIDGE BUILDER

An old man going along a highway
Came in the evening cold and gray
To a chasm vast and deep and wide.
The old man crossed in the twilight dim
The sullen stream had no fear for him,
But he turned when safe on the other side
And built a bridge to span the tide.

"Old man", said a pilgim near
"You are wasting your time with building here.
Your journey will end with the ending of day,
You never again will pass this way,
You have crossed the chasm deep and wide
Why do you build at eventide?"

The old man lifted his old grey head
--- "Good friend, in the way that I have come",
he said,
"There followeth after me today
A youth whose feet must pass this way.
This chasm which has been as naught to me
--- To that fair-haired youth might a pitfall be.
He, too, must cross in the twilight dim,
Good friend, I am building the bridge for him."

William Allen Dromgoole

THE WORLD'S NEED

So many gods, so many creeds,
So many paths that wind and wind,
When just the art of being kind
Is all this sad world needs.

Ella Wheeler Wilcox

ABOU BEN ADHEM

Abou Ben Adhem (may his tribe increase!)
Awoke one night from a deep dream of peace,
And saw, within the moonlight of his room,
Making it rich, and like a lily in bloom,
An angel writing in a book of gold:
Exceeding peace has made Ben Adhem bold,
And to the presence in the room he said,
"What writest thou?" The Vision raised its head,
And with a look made of all sweet accord
Answered, "The names of those who love the Lord."
"And is mine one?" said Abou. "Nay, not so",
Replied the Angel. Abou spoke more low,
But cheerily still; and said, "I pray thee, then,
Write me as one that loves his fellow men."

The Angel wrote and vanished. The next night
It came again with a wakening light,
And showed the names whom love of God had blessed,
And, lo! Ben Adhem's name led all the rest.

James Henry Leigh Hunt

OUTWITTED

He drew a circle and left me out,
Heretic, rebel, a thing to flout;
But love and I had the wit to win,
We drew a circle that took him in.

Edwin Markham

WHAT IS A FRIEND?

What is a friend? I will tell you! It is a person with whom you dare to be yourself. Your soul can go naked with him. He seems to not want you to be better or worse. When you are with him you feel as a prisoner feels who has been declared innocent. You do not have to be on your guard. You can say what you think; express what you feel. He is shocked at nothing, offended at nothing, so long as it is genuinely you. He understands the little contradictions in your nature that lead others to misjudge you. With him you breathe free. You can take off your coat, slip off your shoes. You can avow your little vanities and envies and hates and vicious sparks, your meanness and absurdities, and in opening them up to him they are lost, dissolved in the white ocean of his loyalty. He understands. You do not have to be careful. You can abuse him, neglect him, berate him. Best of all you can keep still with him. It makes no matter. He likes you. He is like water that cleanses all you say. He is like wine that warms you to the bone. He understands. You can weep with him, laugh with him, sin with him, pray with him. Through and beneath it all he sees, knows, and loves you. A friend, I repeat, is the one with whom you dare to be yourself.

Author Unknown

TRUE FRIENDS

Why are true friends so rare?
I ask with a mournful sigh.
I ought to ask instead:
What kind of a friend am I.

Author Unknown

A SUNSET ..... A FRIEND

A breathtaking sunset tonight did unfold,
Reflecting its glow across the shining sea.
With the truest colors of crimson, pink, and gold
Never made here on earth by you or by me.
Its beauty spread warmth to pale clouds and sky,
Farther than can ever be seen with the eye.
Sunsets linger but minutes, so stop rushing and
be filled
With its messages which will leave you much more
than just thrilled.

A sunset is much like a friendship so true,
For its discovery requires looking beyond and
through
Your own troubles and care;
To linger with others, to give and to share.
Only inches from you is this "one" you could know,
One with a sunset-like, crimson glow.
The joy, warmth, and love together all blend
Into a wonderful thing called a friend.

"Kip"
Enid Liebinger
Camp Sealth counselor,
1959

THE TEST OF FRIENDSHIP

The test of friendship is its fidelity when every charm of fortune and environment has been spent away, and the bare, undraped character alone remains; if love still holds steadfast, and the joy of companionship survives in such an hour, the fellowship becomes a beautiful prophecy of immortality.

Hamilton W. Mabie

I SHALL NOT PASS THIS WAY AGAIN

Through this toilsome world, alas!
Once and only once I pass;
If a kindness I may show,
If a good deed I may do
To a suffering fellow man,
Let me do it while I can.
No delay, for it is plain
I shall not pass this way again.

Author Unknown

A PAL

I don't know what it means to you
To have a pal, but, gee,
I want to say it's surely true
It means a lot to me.

Author Unknown

IT'S UP TO YOU

Have you made someone sad?
What have you done with the day you had?
God gave it to you to do just as you would.
Did you do what was wicked or do what was good?
Did you hand out a smile, or just give them a frown?
Did you lift someone up or push someone down?
Did you lighten some load or some progress impede?
Did you look for a rose or just gather a weed?
What did you do with your beautiful day?
God gave it to you,
Did you throw it away?

Author Unknown

IT IS MY JOY

It is my joy in life to find
At every turning of the road
The strong arm of a comrade kind
To help me onward with my load;
But since I have no gold to give
And love alone must make amends,
My only prayer is while I live
God make me worthy of my Friends.

Frank D. Sherman

FRIENDSHIP

Oh, the comfort - the inexpressible comfort of
feeling safe with a person,
Having neither to weigh thoughts,
Nor measure words - but pouring them
All right out - just as they are,
Chaff and grain together;
Certain that a faithful hand will
Take and sift them,
Keep what is worth keeping
And with a breath of kindness,
Blow the rest away.

Dinah Maria Mulock Craik

FRIENDSHIP

As to the value of other things, most men
differ;
Concerning friendship, all have the same opinion.
What sweetness is left in life, if you take away
friendship?
Robbing life of friendship is like robbing the
world of the sun.
A true friend is more to be esteemed than
kinsfolk.

Cicero

CHOOSE YOUR FRIEND WISELY

Choose your friend wisely,
Test your friend well,
True friends, like rarest gems
Prove hard to tell;
Winter him, summer him,
Know your friend well.

Author Unknown

WE'D FIND

We'd find each face was beautiful,
However plain it seems,
If, looking past the dull outside
We saw the wistful dreams.

Author Unknown

A WORD TO THE LIVING

It isn't enough to say in our hearts
That we like a man for his ways.
It isn't enough that we fill our minds
With paeans of silent praise.
Nor is it enough that we honor a man,
As our confidence upward mounts.
It's going right up to the man himself
And telling him so, that counts.
If a man does a work you really admire,
Don't leave a kind word unsaid
In fear that to do so might make him vain,
And cause him to "lose his head".
But reach out your hand and tell him, "Well done!"
And see how his gratitude swells.
It isn't the flowers we strew on the grave,
It's the word to the living that tells.

Author Unknown

TELL HIM SO

If you hear a kind word spoken
Of some worthy soul you know,
It may fill his heart with sunshine
If you only tell him so.

If a deed, however humble,
Helps you on your way to go,
Seek the one whose hand has helped you,
Seek him out and tell him so.

Author Unknown

UNCOUNTED GOLD

A man can own uncounted gold
And land and buildings tall,
But love is just to give away.
It can't be owned at all.

Author Unknown

FRIENDSHIP QUOTES
(Authors Unknown)

A friend is one who knows all about you, and likes you just the same.

Friendship is a state of being friends.

A friend is one attached to another by esteem, respect, and affection; an intimate.

A friend is one who understands
What's in the heart of you,
Who knows and overlooks your faults
Because they're a part of you.

A SONG

I breathed a song into the air
It fell to earth, I know not where...
And the song, from beginning to end,
I found again in the heart of a friend.

Henry Wadsworth Longfellow

FRIENDSHIP

Friendship is like a hearth fire burning bright,
A softly-glowing place apart,
Where one from outer chill returning
May pause awhile to warm his heart.

Author Unknown

CONVEY THY LOVE

Convey thy love to thy friend as an arrow to the mark; to stick there - not as a ball against the wall to rebound back to thee.

Author Unknown

AM I THE ONLY ONE

Am I the only one in life
Who always seems to stand apart?
Or is it everyone who feels
A little lonesome in his heart?

Author Unknown

CHARITY

There is so much good in the worst of us,

And so much bad in the best of us,

That it ill behooves any of us

To find fault with the rest of us.

Author Unknown

BE COURTEOUS

Be courteous to all, but intimate with few, and let these few be well tried before you give them your confidence. True friendship is a plant of slow growth and must undergo and withstand the shocks of adversity before it is entitled to the appellation.

George Washington

...of Leadership

LEADERSHIP

A real guide - a true leader is one who has been over the trail and knows all the twists and turns. The real joy of living comes from being able to go down to the foot of the trail and guide a group up to the heights that you know and love.

You lead the group out on the open trail, that trail that has no end.

Jay B. Nash

THOU ART THE GUARDIAN

THOU ART THE GUARDIAN: It shall be thy task
To keep the newly kindled fire alight;
To know the earth, the sea, the stars above;
Hold happiness; seek beauty; follow right;
Offer a friendly hand to all who ask.
And, day by day,
Lead sister feet along the golden way -
The road that leads to work and health and love.

Camp Fire Guardian's Certificate

PARADOX

It is a paradox of life that we
save that which we give away.

Luther Gulick

LORD, MAKE A REGULAR MAN OUT OF ME

This I would like to be - braver and bolder,
Just a bit wiser because I am older,
Just a bit kinder to those I may meet,
Just a bit manlier taking defeat;
This for the New Year my wish and my plea -
Lord, make a regular man out of me.

This I would like to be - just a bit finer,
More of a smiler and less of a whiner,
Just a bit quicker to stretch out my hand
Helping another who's struggling to stand,
This is my prayer for the New Year to be,
Lord, make a regular man out of me.

This I would like to be - just a bit fairer,
Just a bit better, and just a bit squarer,
Not quite so ready to censure and blame,
Quicker to help every man in the game,
Not quite so eager men's failings to see,
Lord, make a regular man out of me.

This I would like to be - just a bit truer,
Less of the wisher and more of the doer,
Broader and bigger, more willing to give,
Living and helping my neighbor to live!
This for the New Year my prayer and my plea -
Lord, make a regular man out of me.

From THE LIGHT OF FAITH
by Edgar A. Guest

THE POWER OF EXAMPLE

If a boy lives with criticism, he learns to condemn.
If a boy lives with hostility, he learns to fight.
If a boy lives with fear, he learns to be apprehensive.
If a boy lives with jealousy, he learns to feel guilty.
BUT -
If a boy lives with Tolerance, he learns to be patient.
If a boy lives with Encouragement, he learns to be confident.
If a boy lives with Praise, he learns to be appreciative.
If a boy lives with Acceptance, he learns to love.
If a boy lives with Approval, he learns to like himself.
If a boy lives with Recognition, he learns to have a goal.
If a boy lives with Honesty, he learns about the truth.
If a boy lives with Fairness, he learns about justice.
If a boy lives with Security, he learns to have faith.
If a boy lives with friendliness, he learns that the world is a pretty nice place to live in.

Author Unknown
Boys Brotherhood Republic
of New York

UNREMEMBERED ACTS

That best portion of a good man's life, -
His little nameless, unremembered acts
Of kindness and of love.

William Wordsworth

A LEADER

A leader is best when people barely know he exists,
Not so good when people obey and acclaim him,
Worse when they despise him.
Fail to honor people,
They fail to honor you;
But of a good leader, who talks little,
When his work is done, his aim fulfilled,
They will all say, "We did this ourselves".

Lao-tse
Women's Press
January, 1948

LEADERS

Each man who bravely fights his way,
Who tackles problems with a vim,
Adds just a little to the strength
Of all those coming after him.

Rebecca McCann

INSCRIPTION ON THE STATUE OF LIBERTY

"Give me your tired, your poor,
Your huddled masses yearning to breathe free,
The wretched refuse of your teeming shore,
Send these, the homeless, tempest-tossed to me:
I lift my lamp beside the golden door."

Emma Lazarus

SUCCESS

"To laugh often and love much;
To win respect of intelligent persons
and the affection of children;
To earn the approbation of honest critics
and endure the betrayal of false friends;
To appreciate beauty;
To find the best in others;
To give of one's self; to leave the world
a bit better, whether it be a healthy
child, a garden patch, or a redeemed
social condition, to have played and
laughed with enthusiasm, and sung
with exultation, to know even one life
has breathed easier because you have
lived ----
this is to have succeeded!"

Author Unknown

THE COUNSELOR

Lord, who am I to teach the way
To little children day by day
So prone, myself, to go astray?
I teach them knowledge, but I know
How faint the flicker and how low
The candle of my knowledge glow.
I teach them power to will and do
But only now to learn anew
My own great weakness through and through.
I teach them love for all mankind
And all God's creatures, but I find
My loves comes lagging still behind.
Lord, if their guide I still must be
Oh, let the children see
The teacher leaning hard on Thee.

Author Unknown

SERVICE

A child's kiss
Set on thy sighing lips shall
make thee glad;
A poor man served by thee
shall make thee rich;
A sick man helped by thee
shall make thee strong;
Thou shalt be served thyself
by every sense
Of service which thou
renderest.

Elizabeth Barrett Browning
From: A Drama of Exile

THIS IS MY COUNTRY

God grant that not only the love of liberty but a thorough knowledge of the rights of man may pervade all the nations of the earth, so that a philosopher may set foot anywhere on its surface and say: "This is my country!"

Benjamin Franklin

A SPORTSMAN

A sportsman is a man who doesn't boast or
quit; nor make excuses when he fails.
He is a cheerful loser, and a quiet winner.
He plays fair and as well as he can.
He enjoys the pleasure of risk.
He gives his opponent the benefit of the doubt
and he values the game itself more
highly than the result.

Author Unknown

THE AMERICAN CREED

I believe in the United States of America as a government of the people, by the people, for the people; whose just powers are derived from the consent of the governed; a democracy in a republic; a sovereign nation among many sovereign states; a perfect union, one and inseparable; established upon the principles of freedom, equality, justice, and humanity for which American patriots sacrificed their lives and their fortunes.

I therefore believe it is my duty to my country to love it; to support its constitution, obey its laws; to respect its flag, and to defend it against all enemies.

William Tyler Page
Accepted April 3, 1918 by the
House of Representatives on behalf
of the American people.

GOD BLESS THE FLAG

God bless the flag! Let it float and fill
The sky with its beauty; our heart strings thrill
To the low sweet chant of its wind-swept bars,
And the chorus of all its clustering stars.

Author Unknown

TO THE BOYS OF AMERICA

Of course what we have a right to expect from the American boy is that he shall turn out to be a good American man. Now, the chances are strong that he won't be much of a man unless he be a good deal of a boy. He must not be a coward, or a weakling, a bully, a shirk, or a prig. He must work hard and play hard. He must be clean-minded and clean-lived, and able to hold his own under all circumstances and against all comers. It is only on these conditions that he will grow into the kind of man of whom America can really be proud....In short, in life, as in a football game, the principle to follow is: Hit the line hard; don't foul and don't shirk, but hit the line hard.

Theodore Roosevelt
from
"The American Boy"

ADDITIONAL SELECTIONS

SELECTED REFERENCES

CARNEGIE, DOROTHY, Dale Carnegie's Scrapbook. New York, N. Y.: Simon Schuster, 1959.

EDGAR, MARY S., Under Open Skies. Toronto, Canada: Clarke, Irwin and Co., Ltd., 1957.

FELLEMAN, HAZEL, The Best Loved Poems of the American People. Garden City, N. Y.: Garden City Books, 1936.

GROVER, EDWIN O., Nature Lover's Knapsack. New York, N. Y.: Thomas Y. Crowell Company, 1927.

HENRY, RALPH and PANNELL, LUCILLE, My American Heritage. Chicago, Illinois: Rand McNally and Company, 1949.

KOPPLIN, DOROTHEA, S., Something To Live By. Garden City, N. Y.: Garden City Books, 1959.

MATTOON, LAURA and BRAGDON, HELEN D., Services For The Open. New York, N. Y.: Association Press, 1947.

McCANN, REBECCA, Cheerful Cherub. New York, N. Y.: Covici-Friede, 1932.

MORRISON, JAMES DALTON, Masterpieces of Religious Verse. New York, N. Y.: Harper and Brothers, Publishers, 1948.

PEASE, HARRIET WELLS, Altars Under The Sky. Nashville, Tenn., Abingdon Press, 1942.

SECHRIST, ELIZABETH HOUGH, Poems For Red Letter Days. Philadelphia, Pa.: Macrae Smith Company, 1951.

SILLIMAN, VINCENT, Editor, We Speak Of Life. Boston, Mass.: Beacon Press, 1955.

THOMPSON, BLANCHE J., More Silver Pennies. New York, N. Y.: The Macmillan Company, 1938.

THOMPSON, BLANCHE J., Silver Pennies. New York, N. Y.: Simon and Schuster, 1950.

WATSON, LILLIAN EICHLER, Light From Many Lamps. New York, N. Y.: Simon and Schuster, 1951.

WEBB, KENNETH B., Light From A Thousand Camp Fires. Martinsville, Indiana: American Camping Association, 1960.

AUTHOR INDEX

Page

SUBJECT AND TITLE INDEX

CAMP

BEAUTY AND NATURE

FAITH AND INSPIRATION

FRIENDSHIP

LEADERSHIP